THE FOOT READING COACH

THE FOOT READING COACH

JANE SHEEHAN

www.footreading.com
www.findafootreader.com

Also by the same author:
Let's Read Our Feet!

The Foot Reading Coach by Jane Sheehan
First Edition 2008

Copyright 2008 © Jane Sheehan

Published by
Jane Sheehan
Manor Beeches,
Manor Gardens
Maids Moreton
Buckinghamshire
MK18 1QA, England
www.footreading.com
www.findafootreader.com

Some names used in the examples in this book have been changed to protect the identity of those individuals.

A CIP catalogue record for this book is available from the British Library.

ISBN 978-0-9550593-1-5

Design by Nicki Averill Design & Illustration

Contents

About the Author

Jane Sheehan is the UK's leading **foot reader** – she reads personality traits through the shape and form of feet and toes. Jane qualified as a reflexologist in 1999 and first became interested in foot reading after a **reflexology** session had a profound impact on her, and she decided to find out more about the link between feet and wellbeing.

Jane developed her foot reading skills through a combination of experience and learning from specialist sources. After four years of practising reflexology and foot reading in her spare time, Jane left her nine-to-five office job and embarked on a career centred on her foot reading **skills**.

The success of Jane's workshops has meant that she has been incredibly busy not just here in the UK but has also worked in the USA, United Arab Emirates, Ireland and Australia (she has already been asked to return) and has made several TV appearances.

- *This Morning* where Jane appeared twice, which came about after Jane read Fern Britton's feet!
- *Today with Des and Mel*
- *Big Brother's Little Brother* and *Morning Glory* with Dermot O'Leary
- *The Afternoon Show* on RTE, Ireland
- *Inside San Diego* and Fox in *The Morning* in America
- *Sama* in Dubai
- *Today Show* on Channel Nine, Australia.

In addition, Jane is a regular on regional radio stations and has had various articles in such publications as *The Daily Mail*, *Top Sante*, *New Woman* and Jane's foot reading skill was hailed as one of *Sunday Times*' 'Top Ten Health Trends'.

Jane's first book *Let's Read Our Feet!* demonstrates how to read the hidden messages in feet. It shows how the shape of feet and toes can not only tell a lot about a person's personality, but also help them to improve areas of our lives that they are unhappy with. Jane's second book *The Foot Reading Coach* gives coaching tips for foot readers to assist with the process of moving forward.

Jane Sheehan's work includes:

- hosting Foot Reading parties which are fast becoming the modern alternative to the commercial 'cosmetics sales' parties for today's busy lifestyles
- continuing to develop her reflexology work
- performing corporate team building workshops
- assisting with product launches
- conducting after dinner speeches and talks to a wide cross section of the community.

Jane is now working with **corporate clients** in a variety of ways – from offering individual readings for personal development to working with **teams** in order to find the best way for them to work together, based on the personalities identified through their readings.

Her websites are **www.footreading.com** and **www.findafootreader.com**

Chapter 1
Introduction

The assumption that I have made in writing this book is that you have already learned how to foot read from my first book *Let's Read Our Feet!* Whilst it is not essential to have read it because the coaching methods can stand alone, I've divided the coaching methods up using the related toe that may trigger a need to use those methods.

If you've already read *Let's Read Our Feet!* skip this chapter and go straight to chapter 2!

How did you begin? 1.1

Once upon a time, I trained as a reflexologist. What makes a normal, healthy, grounded, cynical, down-to-earth person volunteer themselves to give up a year of their life to study how the organs of the body are reflected on the feet – I mean the feet for goodness sake – and then learn how to poke the feet to help rebalance those organs?

Think about it. "Erm, excuse me, I just want to massage below the ball of the foot to help your liver condition." It sounds crazy, doesn't it?

Then try to bring in the emotional aspects of a physical illness: "Your lower back pain relates to your feeling you don't have enough financial support in your life".

You can almost hear the men in white coats coming to get you, can't you?

So here's my story about what led me from a healthy disrespect to all things 'new age' to becoming a big proponent of the self-help and complementary movement. Note that I'm not saying 'alternative'. That's a step too far for me at this stage in my life.

Once upon a time, my friend Claudine told me that she fancied having reflexology for her birthday. I thought it was a beauty treatment, so I made appointments for the pair of us to get pampered. Or so I thought. Claudine's there having her treatment and they're telling her things about her health that I knew but I couldn't fathom out how they knew. True things, by the way, nothing airy fairy. So then it was my turn. As soon as they started touching my big toe, I had tears streaming down my face. I had no control over them. Every time they moved away from my big toe, it stopped. Move back again and it would start up again. It was repeatable on both feet. I had to know more.

I enrolled on a reflexology course with Chiltern School of Reflexology. From day one I was fascinated. It was like nothing I'd ever come across before. I read anything and everything I could get my hands on related to reflexology. At the end of the course we had to do 65 hours case studies. Every one of my case studies had huge emotional reactions. By this stage I understood the physical reactions but I still didn't understand why they would have an emotional reaction. What is the connection between the emotions and the feet?

1.2   Weird experiences

Well, the more I practiced reflexology, the more intensely I would concentrate, looking for both the physical and the emotional reaction. One day, a really weird thing happened. I was treating a client when all of a sudden I became aware of the sensation of my throat swelling up but it was only on one side and I knew it wasn't mine. I can't phrase it better than that. So I asked her, "What's happening with your throat?," and she said "It's funny you should say that, it feels like I've swallowed a golf ball," and I indicate to her that it's only on one side. She's amazed. She confirms the fact. I was so excited by the experience that I forgot to work the reflex that related to the sensation. This was a Friday.

The following Monday I see the lady again and she tells me she had a terrible weekend. She was rushed into hospital with suspected meningitis. Her throat had swollen up and she'd got a rash, but it was gone as quickly as it had arisen. They kept her overnight for observation but she was fine. It taught me a huge lesson. If you get such a sensation, you have to work the reflex. You're picking up the sensation for a reason. I did know this lady had belonged to a cult and I did know that emotionally she always felt she could not speak her own truth. I can see the emotional and physical connection.

Over time you get used to having these sensations and you see them as a part of your treatment. In the early days I would only pick up things if I was 'hands on' but now I've learned to do a quick body scan myself to see how I'm feeling before I start a treatment or a foot reading and then I can be much more aware when a new sensation is there. I can more easily establish if it is mine or theirs. Since I've been practising this, I do sometimes pick up sensations when I'm not hands on. The only times I've had such sensations when I've not had my head in therapist mode was when I walked into an accountancy office where a lady had just had a car crash and she was still in shock and when I've met someone who later turned out to be bad news for me.

I know I'm not the only person who experiences this sort of thing. I picked up an enquiry via a reflexology blog where a lady was having similar experiences where she was picking up the sensations as colours. I was able to share my knowledge with her and we've been friends ever since.

The best advice I can give you when you are starting out in reflexology is 'notice what you notice'. Try not to jump to conclusions or give things meanings. Just watch and observe and build up your body of knowledge. If someone hands you a theory, check to see when it doesn't work, as well as when it does work.

1.3 How did you get from Reflexology to Foot Reading?

At the end of my reflexology course, I was still non-the-wiser about why I'd had my emotional reaction or why my case study clients were also having emotional reactions just through having their feet worked. There had to be a relationship between the feet and the emotions.

At that time in my life I didn't know about the mind/body/spirit connection. Someone gave me a copy of *You Can Heal Your Life*, by Louise Hay. In it there is a list of illnesses, the emotional imbalance that, if left undealt with, could create the illness, and a positive affirmation to help you release that emotional imbalance.

At first I just wanted to laugh at the idea. What about viruses? What about bacteria? But the more I was seeing clients, the more I'd be drawn to checking out their illness using this book and with a few questions found out how the emotional imbalance was there for them. I started giving the affirmations as homework.

After I'd accepted the mind/body/spirit connection, someone gave me a book by Imre Somogyi called *Toe Reading*. He'd interviewed 5000 people about their toe shapes and their personality and came up with a toe alphabet that you can use to interpret personality and emotions. He'd allocated each of the toes one of the five elements and used that as his basic pattern. I was fascinated. I quickly learned his toe alphabet and started reading anyone and everyone who'd let me. It got to the stage where I'd go to a party and I'd get a foot before I'd get a drink! The more I used it, the more I fine-tuned it. Some of the meanings of the toes I didn't 100% agree with and I started to try out different nuances until I arrived at the ones I thought were consistently accurate for me.

Then I was given the book *Language of the Feet*, by Chris Stormer. I loved it. I don't use exactly the same toe meanings but I do use a lot of the meanings for blemishes that she has in this book and I've added it to my existing body of knowledge. Like with all learning you pick up what resonates with you and you discard what doesn't. I later went on one of Chris Stormer's workshops and she said something about how you take the map of the body and put it on the foot or the face or the hands and in that moment it was like a light bulb going on. Take the emotional map of the foot and put it back on the body – so then when someone's clutching their side you can see the emotional background. And what if we shrink the map onto one of the toes so that you are no longer just reading the energy of that toe, but we can also fine-tune the reading to see much more detail. Fantastic. Thank you Chris!

How closely is foot reading related to reflexology? Is it very different to palm reading?   1.4

It was reflexology that got me started and it's useful to know reflexology when you're doing a foot reading. Reflexology is more about working the acupressure points on the feet to bring the body back into balance. You have a physical map of the body superimposed on the foot. With foot reading, you have an emotional map superimposed on the foot. Rather than pressing the points, you look at the points, you don't have to touch. Mind you, occasionally I will poke a toe to see whether it is touching the ground or not. Whilst I read the emotional map, I also keep my knowledge of reflexology at hand because sometimes you can see something that you know is not emotional but has become physical and so you can offer that information too or offer some 'homework' so that they can work on it themselves.

When I'm doing reflexology, I keep the foot reading knowledge to hand so that I can ask a seemingly innocent question that can plant the seed for change emotionally and thus help to tackle the physical problem from different angles. I am a great believer in the multi-pronged approach to health. It's not enough to deal with the emotion and leave the physical alone. It's not enough to deal with the physical and leave the emotion alone.

As for palm reading – I don't know anything about it. I'm sure it would be similar yet different because the meridians running in the hands are different from those in the feet. Your feet are about where you want to go in life and your hands are about what you want to do in life. I've had a few palm readers come on my courses over the years and they tell me it is different in some ways yet similar in others. For example, I have the right foot as the past but the left hand to them represents the past. The white moons on the toe nail base, in both foot reading and palm reading represent having time to appreciate the aesthetics.

Also, palm reading is often assumed to relate to reading the future. I do not read the future, but focus on the past and the present.

Why the feet? In your view, why do feet reflect so much about us? 1.5

Why not the feet? Everything about us reflects something about us, from the way we dress to where we live. Think about how you walk when you are angry – you stamp your feet harder to the ground. Think about how you walk when you are depressed – you hunch your shoulders and drag your feet and use a different part of your foot. Think about how you walk when you are happy – light steps. We're on our feet so much and they are impacted by every step we take and the way in which we take those steps. That's why I see foot reading as looking at the impact of what has happened to you and the impact of what is currently happening to you. If you've got a major life issue but you're handling it really well, it's less likely to show on your feet than if you are struggling with it.

What is reflexology's role in foot reading and vice versa? 1.6

Are you kidding? They go together like mind and body. When you do reflexology, you are working the foot to help bring balance back into the body. When you do a foot reading you are focusing on the emotions and helping to bring balance to the emotions. When the body is out of balance, there will also be an emotional imbalance. When the emotions are out of balance, there will also be a physical imbalance. It's all connected. So in my mind a single pronged attack to an emotional or physical problem is not enough. You have to treat the whole.

If you have bunions or a big toe leaning towards the little toe then you are bending over backwards doing far too much for others and not enough for yourself. You must help both the emotional imbalance that leads to them overdoing the helping and you must help the big toe physically back to health.

When you see a fungal infection of the toe nail, you need to assist with the releasing of the emotional problems relating to other people interfering, telling them what to think, nagging, hindering their progress. Physically you need to look at their diet as there may be a digestive problem arising allowing the fungal infection to take hold, and maybe you also need to treat the fungal infection topically. A combination of all three will help shift it completely. Do only one and it may come back.

Sometimes when I'm doing reflexology, I have what I call an 'intentional conversation' where I'm using my foot reading knowledge but not actually saying exactly what I see, but planting a question to get the client to explore the issue. When I'm doing foot reading, I may sometimes offer a bit of reflexology to help release an emotional issue through a physical route.

I've just done a foot reading workshop – let me share with you the comments I'm getting in unsolicited emails from the participants:

'Thanks Jane
Am really really enjoying reading my clients feet, it is giving me so much more!!!
love Claire'

Linda said:
'After the last course, I offered my services at the nursery school where I work part time. They were having a fun day before the end of term and the head-teacher took me up on my offer. Thank goodness the mums weren't being charged. It was enjoyable and rewarding but harder work than I had ever imagined. One young mum had such potential,

leadership, "manipulative" toes and other talents. She really needed someone to reinforce what she really wanted but didn't quite have the confidence to go for. Not only that, a fortune-teller had told her the same things. I learned so much about two mums whose children had been in my group, how they had become friends bringing their children to school and how they had supported one another. They had formed a bond and after the session I felt a close bond with them and there was much hugging. It also helped me to understand their children's behaviour. It's a wonderful moment when you read something in a foot and the person gives you her explanation – a real eureka moment.'

Sarah said:
'With my mind still buzzing from the stimulation and challenges of the past w/e I thought I'd just 'mail you to say THANK YOU for a most interesting, CURIOUS, funny but deadly serious course! How like all of Life! Fascinating...
And Jane , you have so much vitality is this because you have read your feet and 'de-fragged' yourself, thrown off all the unwanted rubbish as it were!?'

Tracey said:
'Just a quick e-mail to say thank you for a wonderful weekend. Words cannot express how much I enjoyed this enlightening weekend. You are an inspiration in more ways than one. I have already started foot reading. Remember I told you about the lady with the fungal nail. I read this for her and a few other things I say and she was flabbergasted. I also did a little with my friend who was shocked and very intrigued by what I had seen just from her feet. I do hope that our paths cross again in the very near future.'

Dinah said:
'Just to say thank you for a really informative, eye-opening day which was relaxed and great fun into the bargain.

I was amazed today when I examined my son's feet to find a reddish-brown spot at about 3 months up in the right foot big toe nail-bed. I realised that this coincided almost exactly with the worsening of his OCD symptoms in December, about which he had felt really fed up and angry with himself. It being in the centre of the nail I assumed it was related to his 'actions' which is very appropriate with repetitive behaviour. I was pleased to see that the last 6 weeks or so of nail growth was normal, as this is the period we have been receiving treatment from the behavioural therapist, so clearly he has been feeling less angry since.

My daughter told me she 'liked her feet, but wished they were bigger' (which is better than 6 months ago when she told me she hated them!). So I am now working on giving her even more recognition for all her achievements!

So it has been lovely to put the theory into practise straight away – I still feel I have a very long way to go, but I'm determined to get there.'

Or how about from a radio interviewer:
'I was on your website yesterday and it looks amazing! I even sent on some 'feet facts' to my friends so they could pick out which ones they were.and I never do that when I'm researching! It just really caught my interest as everyone has an opinion on their feet! Most people I know have foot phobias. Personally, I love mine and would love you to read them!! From Rachel'

1.7   Why do you love feet and how do you feel about your own?

This is a common misconception about me. It's not that I love feet. I don't see feet as feet anymore. I see them as a story waiting to be read. I'm fascinated by people, always have been. I love knowing secrets too. The feet to me are just another tool for 'people watching'.

Asking me how I feel about my own feet is a trick question. It's one of the first questions I ask of people when I'm doing a foot reading, because how you feel about your feet is how you feel about yourself. One person said to me, "I love my feet, they take me where I want to go," and I asked, "How's your career?" "On the up." I can tell because of the words she uses. A lot of people hate their feet so I ask them to explain what specifically they hate. It gives me useful info. I have a friend who has been on a diet ever since I met her even though to me there's nothing wrong with her. She said, "I hate my feet, they're really wide and lumpy and bumpy!" I don't see that when I look at her feet either. She's just revealing how she feels about herself.

How do I feel about my own feet? I hardly think about them except when I'm teaching a class and then if I have sandals on I feel really exposed because I know they can really see everything about me. Mind you, I'm getting used to it now! When I first started teaching foot reading I always wore boots up to the knee! Now I'm OK in sandals. Don't tell Donna Sozio – she's a shoe reader and she'll be analysing me like a shot!

How do your methods differ from others?   1.8

I teach lots of people how to do foot reading. Not just reflexologists either. Let me tell you this – every single one of them will do foot reading differently despite having the same teacher. Guaranteed. That's because we're all individual, we all have our own perspective on life, our own way of expressing things, our own life experiences. This all goes into the mix of what makes us a good foot reader or a good reflexologist. It's not about comparing ourselves to others, it's about living to our full potential whatever that may be.

Wasn't it Judy Garland who said, "Be a first rate version of yourself, not a second rate version of someone else!"

I use foot reading in more than one way:
- To understand my reflexology clients better
- To have intentional conversations with my clients
- As a foot reading in its own right
- To bring therapy to people who wouldn't otherwise seek it, through meeting them at a foot party
- Foot Reading Parties
- Corporate Events
- Management Training seminars using foot reading for team building exercises

1.9 Is foot reading difficult to learn, given the many variants?

I don't think so. Mind you, after eight years I am still learning! I teach all the series of techniques on day one, then on day two we have lots of practice. Initially the students are worried that they don't know anything and I encourage them to use their notes and take the time to look things up, but by the second reading they realise that they can do it.

I teach it in a way that they can logically work out an answer even when they come across something they haven't seen before. After that, it's all practice and memorising the techniques. The more you look, the more you see. I'm at the stage now where I show my student something that to me is glaringly obvious and they ask me if it will always appear so subtly!

I do believe anyone can learn it. I've even taught 14 to 17 year olds and 18 to 21 year olds at the Dubai Ladies Club. Imagine being in a country where they are covered from head to toe and you can only see the feet and eyes – foot reading really comes into its own. The Qu'ran forbids fortune telling, but it's not fortune telling (you're reading the impact of emotions and personality, not the future) and it helps you to understand a person quickly and build a deep feeling of trust by knowing the best way to approach that person.

How can foot reading be incorporated into other therapies?   1.10

I believe that allowing your client to notice things for themselves will help them far more than if you try to 'fix' them. If you can hold a mirror up to the person and they can really notice things about themselves, they have all the tools at their disposal to be able to bring about change by using their own answers. For me, foot reading is that mirror. If you are a massage therapist, you can see the shoulders are knotted, but as a foot reader, you have more information about what factors in their life are stressing them. If you can get the person to look again at these areas of their life then they now have two ways of getting back into balance – the massage and the ideas of how they can reduce the initial stresses. If they are complaining of back pain but you can't find a physical imbalance in the back, then you can use the foot reading and look at what areas of their life they are lacking support.

If you are a pedicurist you can see from the feet which areas of their life the client is having difficulties – you can decide you only want to have a fun day today so you avoid talking about that and ask questions about the other areas, avoiding the big issues. Or if you want lots of repeat business, you can see the areas that are issues and you can ask a question and listen without judgement. In this way, the clients feel they are heard and see much more value in your work than just having their nails done.

If you're a reflexologist you often see things on the feet that you've been trained to understand as a physical issue, but you know that it just doesn't fit. Now with foot reading you have a much deeper way of tackling it because you can decide to look at the underlying emotions and work with that instead or as well.

1.11 Does this mean our feet change significantly over our lifetime depending on our experiences or are these things we can't change?

Feet are changing all the time. Even during a foot reading I can see the changes through an involuntary movement, a relaxation of the muscle tension, a change in colour/circulation. You've got 26 bones in your foot all connected by a complex network of tendons, muscles and connective tissue. Even though your feet have stopped growing, you can go up or down a shoe size or width. This is because of the tension or relaxation of these muscles. And what causes this tension or relaxation? Your general emotional state and what is happening in your life. Lots can change but some things don't change. It's the old nature versus nurture argument. You're born with a core personality but sometimes you're taught to suppress it, or you're not encouraged to live to your full potential. That's why I love looking at babies' feet to see their potential and why I love looking at older people's feet to see their story. Some people's feet look far too young for their age. There is the proof if ever you needed it that having a good attitude can keep you young! Or as my Pops would say, "It's not what happens to you in life, it's how you handle it that counts."

The top ten secrets that your feet reveal about you   **1.12**

As a foot reader practising since 1999, I am often asked to talk about what secrets the feet reveal. Here I reveal the top ten questions I am most often asked.

Secret 1: What does it mean if I have a bunion?   1.12.1

Bunions are telling you that you are bending over backwards doing too much for others and not enough for yourself! The degree to which the big toe is deformed towards the little toe shows the degree that you are out of balance in this area of your life. Ask yourself, what would I be doing with my time if I had more time for me. Many people with bunions can't answer this. Until they work out what they really want to spend their time on for themselves, they will continue doing too much for others. If you want some clues as to what you would possibly enjoy doing if you had more time, think back to what you did when you were a child in the school holidays. Perhaps you could spend more time doing that now?

Secret 2: What does it mean if I have wide feet?   1.12.2

Very wide feet are what I call the 'carthorse' foot! This person is very hard working. They are constantly doing things and find it very difficult to sit down and do nothing. If I offer you a cup of tea, you will be getting the cups out of the cupboard to help me rather than sitting back and letting me wait on you.

Secret 3: What does it mean if I have narrow feet?   1.12.3

Very narrow feet are what I call the 'princess' foot! You are much happier sitting back and letting others run around after you. 'Peel me a grape!' You are very good at delegating to others without appearing to do so! You appreciate the good things in life.

1.12.4   Secret 4: What does it mean if I have a high arch?
High arches are commonly found on people with strong inner resources. You enjoy spending time on your own. That's not to say that you aren't sociable, but if you do go to a party, you need the next day as quiet time to re-energise. You are very resourceful but find it hard to accept help from others because you feel you can do it all yourself.

1.12.5   Secret 5: What does it mean if I have flat feet?
Your flat feet are showing that you love the company of others. You are very sociable and you just don't like being left on your own. You need lots of support in your life. You're happy to accept help from others... Lots of it!

1.12.6   Secret 6: What does it mean if my feet have grown a shoe size?
Even though your feet have stopped growing, your feet can grow a shoe size because of a relaxation of tension in the tendons and ligaments of the feet. When your feet go up a shoe size, it is because something has changed in your life and you now want recognition for your merits. You're much happier to thrust yourself into the limelight. I know one person whose feet grew like this when she gave up her administration job to become a teacher.

1.12.7   Secret 7: What does it mean if my feet have shrunk a shoe size?
It is possible for your feet to shrink a shoe size because of tension in the tendons and ligaments of the feet. When your feet shrink a shoe size, it is because something has changed in your life and you now feel that you want to take your time to assess situations and watch what is happening before you push yourself forward. You no longer need recognition and value your privacy more. You want to take more of a back-seat role.

Secret 8: What does it mean if I have athlete's foot?   1.12.8

If you have athlete's foot you have developed a tendency to let things get under your skin. You experience extreme irritability. It annoys you that people constantly interfere and doubt and question your ideas. Why are you letting them bother you? Each toe has a meaning assigned to it, once you learn their meanings, you can further refine your interpretation based upon which toes the athlete's foot is occurring.

Secret 9: What does it mean if I have smelly feet?   1.12.9

This is what I call the "skunk" effect! You are trying to make more space for yourself by driving people away with the smell! You often find this on teenagers who are fed up with the rules: 'be back by half ten', 'don't do that', 'do your homework first', 'no you can't have your belly button pierced!' You also find it on carers of a dependent relative where their own personal freedom is restricted by their duty and responsibility. How can you build some more freedom into your life?

Secret 10: What does it mean if I have a gap between my big toe and my second toe?   1.12.10

You have delayed reactions between your logical reaction and your emotional reaction. You need to learn to make more space to think before you make decisions. Do you find that you often agree to do something and the next day you think 'gosh, why did I agree to do that?,' or someone says something to you and the next day you think 'I can't believe I let them get away with that.' It's just that your first reaction was your logical reaction but you hadn't had time to assimilate how you feel about it. The bigger the gap between these toes, the more the delayed reaction.

1.13   Hungry for more?

- My websites are:
  www.footreading.com
  www.findafootreader.com

- My books are *Let's Read Our Feet!* and of course this one (*The Foot Reading Coach*) which are both available from my website or from amazon.co.uk.

- Hire me to conduct a one or two day workshop for your group

- Arrange a foot reading, or a foot reading party

- Organise a corporate event or team building session

- Books I would recommend:
  Toe Reading, by Imre Somogyi
  Language of the Feet, by Chris Stormer
  Analyzing Personality Patterns through the feet, by M Kruchik. This comes from a different paradigm yet is still easy to grasp.

  There are other books on the subject but these are good to get you started! Happy foot reading

Chapter 2

Before you start – some do's and don'ts

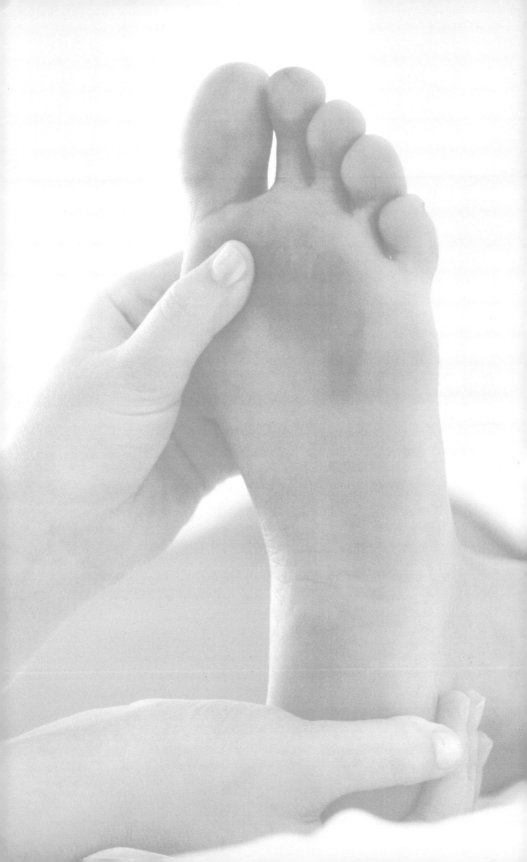

Do maintain the optimum foot reading position

I'm very specific about how I position both myself and my client when I'm foot reading.

The client is sitting on a chair, knees at right-angles, and feet flat on the floor.

Standing opposite the client, I take one small step to my left and then sit on a small foam yoga block.

The reason for the yoga block is so that after years of foot reading and sitting on the floor, I won't damage my hip joints or lower back. When the yoga block was first suggested to me, I avoided getting one for ages, but as soon as I tried one it made such an instant difference to my own comfort that I wish I'd got one sooner. If you're unsure about getting one, try sitting on a book about the height of one of the Harry Potter novels and see what you think.

The reason for positioning myself off-centre and more to my left (the client's right) is two-fold.

- It is rather confrontational to sit directly opposite someone, so I want to alleviate that feeling by sitting off-centre.
- In NLP (Neuro Linguistic Programming), generally, if a person is looking down and to their right then they are accessing their feelings. By sitting on the floor to the client's right then I am encouraging them to look down and to their right thus accessing their own feelings.

When I've finished reading the top of the foot, I then change both my seating position and the client's in order to read the bottom of the foot.

The bottom of the foot represents what is really going on and can often reflect different information to the top. The top of the foot represents what the client perceives is going on behind their back or what they want the world to know.

For the client, I tilt the chair backwards if I am using my La Fuma reclining chair. For me, I get off the floor and onto a stool with wheels. This is so that I am not sitting on the floor all day – by moving positions I can read many feet in one day without compromising my own physical health.

Do ensure your own comfort and remember that you need to be able to maintain that position over a prolonged period.

2.2 Do remember your facial expression

When you first learn to foot read, you get so excited that you have managed to read something, that sometimes in your excitement and enthusiasm you forget to make your facial expression appropriate to the situation!

Example: You've just read that the client's feet show how they are feeling deep hurt connected with a relationship situation but are not expressing it, (bruise on neck of fourth toe). The client admits that they are going through a painful divorce. You're pleased as punch that you got it right and you're grinning like a Cheshire cat. Appropriate or not appropriate – you decide.

So, remember to hide or disguise your inappropriate reaction.

Hide also your shock or judgement. As a foot reader, you build a lot of trust in a short space of time so you are often privy to secrets and to information that maybe this person hasn't even told their nearest and dearest. One of your roles is to act like a confessional where the client is heard but not judged.

It's not all about hiding or disguising your reactions. Sometimes you want to use a facial expression to impress upon the client the information that you are imparting by using a facial expression to underline what you are saying. Or at other times you may want to lighten the mood by using your facial expression.

For example, you have just seen that the two second toes aren't touching the floor which means they are disconnected from their passion in life and disconnected from what they want in life. They feel off track. Rather than getting really heavy about it, you can lighten the mood by saying "You don't know what you want to be when you grow up" and then look up with a cheeky glint in your eye.

In the words of Frank Carson, *"It's the way you tell 'em."*

Do assess curiosity   2.3

When I first started foot reading, I wanted to read anyone and everyone. I'd pounce on any foot available and start to read it. I've read the curious, the cynical and the down-right hostile.

I'm not asking you to curb your enthusiasm, but I'd like to share with you some things I've learned about choosing when to do a reading.

If you want to give a foot reading, first make sure that the person is actually curious to know something about it.

Surprisingly, it's not always appropriate to give a foot reading. I say this as someone who often does impromptu foot readings in cafés, restaurants, airports, even on a plane once! Sometimes the person may have an objection to it for religious reasons. Sometimes the person may have their own agenda for either not wanting you to give the reading, or for wanting you to be incorrect in your reading.

So consequently I now make it my rule to gauge the person's curiosity before deciding whether to expend my time and energy.

2.3.1   Example of when a reading was appropriate

My friend and reflexologist, Sylvia Ferguson, still tells the story about how, on a trip to Derry Airport, we attempted to hire a car via Kings Car Hire desk. All was going well until Wendy (according to her name badge) reached the part on the form where it said 'Occupation'.

"Foot reading?" she exclaimed, "What's that?"

Give me a fiver for every time I've heard that. I've learned that it's far quicker to demonstrate than to explain. I glanced around me. "See that lady in the queue over there?" I point to a flip-flop shod lady in the further of two queues, and then I proceed to read her personality from her foot shape. Even at that distance you can tell quite a lot. Let me tell you this, the minute I start foot reading, I go into my zone. I forget where I am, who I'm with, and I am transported to the story of the foot laid out in front of me. It no longer matters that I'm in the middle of the arrivals hall in Derry. I could be anywhere.

I finish the reading, and become aware that we've drawn attention to ourselves from two pinstripe-suited gentlemen in the nearer of the queues. Sylvia explains that I am a foot reader and we're just reading the feet of the lady across the way from them. Before you can say 'sweaty feet' one of them has his shiny black brogue and matching black sock off, and is raising his foot, can-can style, asking for his own reading. He's not even removed his laptop bag from his shoulder and so he's wobbling around on one leg in imminent danger of falling over!

It was appropriate to demonstrate the foot reading to Wendy as she was curious, and it was also appropriate to do the foot reading for the business man as he also showed his curiosity! Whether it was appropriate to do the reading in the middle of sorting out a car-hire transaction is another matter altogether!

Example of when a reading was inappropriate   2.3.2

I was at a corporate event at Eastnor Castle where I and a group of management consultants were demonstrating our skills and sharing learning experiences. In the evening it was much more informal with a meal followed by drinks in the drawing room. We'd been chatting with a guy who had recently handed over the reins of his company and was wondering what he wanted to do next with his life.

I hadn't been saying much, when he turned to me and said, "The problem with you and foot reading and your ilk is that you so believe in what you do that it is a matter of faith. Doubting what you do is like telling a Christian that they are wrong."

I thought that maybe he didn't understand what I did. I asked him to take his shoes off because I find a demonstration of what I do much more effective than trying to explain it. But he refused. I knew in that moment, that there was no point joining a discussion with this man because he did not want to have a discussion. He just wanted to be right.

If there is no curiosity, you're wasting your time and energy. Walk away.

2.4   Don't take things personally

If people are unhappy, they will try to take away your happiness. They don't even realise they are doing it.

When someone accuses you or your client of something, understand that they are often just talking about themselves.

Try to listen to the meaning behind what was said and how it relates to the person who spoke, rather than how it relates to you or your client.

For example, at a workshop we were asked to describe the hair of the person standing next to us. The lady next to me said "Your hair is very flat and you wish that you could get more lift in it." She wasn't talking about me, she was talking about herself. She'd recently had cancer and her hair was growing back thinly. She'd had it cut into a spikey style and was using product to make it stand up.

2.5   Don't label

Don't let anyone label you!

In this day of political correctness gone mad, it may seem unnecessary to talk about not allowing people to label you. Being labelled diminishes others' ability to see you as the multi-faceted, multi-talented person that you are.

Similarly, don't fall for the labels that have been attached to your clients.

A label doesn't allow for the fact that people can and do change.

Example of why falling for a label is not useful   2.5.1

Once, a friend of mine asked me to give her father a reflexology treatment. He was suffering, she said, from a bad back. He'd been for lots of tests at the hospital but so far no idea why he was in so much pain. I worked the reflexes for the back (medial edge of the foot), looking for anything that felt tender to him, or unusual to me. Nothing. Not a single thing showed up. I'd fallen for the label of 'bad back' instead of just noticing what I could observe for myself. However, he suddenly doubled up in pain. It was so bad that I couldn't continue the treatment. He had to get up and walk around to try to alleviate the pain. He's clutching his lower back and is obviously in agony.

Not being able to continue working on his feet, I fetched a friend of mine who did massage to see if she could help (again the idea of 'bad back'). She said she didn't think it was the back, but asked me to check the kidney reflexes. Sure enough, they were very tender and discoloured and so too was the urinary tract. We sent him back to see his doctor again, this time with information that it may not be his back but his kidneys and urinary tract.

It transpired that he had prostate cancer and it spread to the lymph. I am telling you this story to make you very aware that if you buy into whatever label that has been given, it can stop you from getting to the truth.

Undoing a label   2.6

If a client has bought into the idea that they really are that label, then how can you make them see it differently?

You can ask them, "Would it be OK with you, if you were...," and insert the opposite meaning to the label they consider they are.

For example, the client has been labelled as uncreative, useless at art. "Would it be OK with you if you were creative?"

Or you can point out to them how many instances that you know of when they were the opposite of that or better still, get them to volunteer the information.

"Remember the time that you made a wall hanging?" or "Tell me what was the last thing that you made."

This is a technique that is worth using if the label is no longer helpful or true.

Another method is to keep a diary of only the times when they demonstrate the aptitude of the opposite of that label.

For example, if the label is that they are lazy, then they keep a diary of all the events that show how they are active.

2.7 What coaching is not

Coaching is not about you giving your clients *your* solutions to *their* problems. Let me repeat that. Coaching is NOT about you giving your clients your solutions to their problems.

Don't assume that you have all the answers. Often when you are foot reading you have never met this person before. You don't know anything about them other than what you can see on their feet. You don't know what fun is for them. You don't know their hopes, dreams, and aspirations. You don't know what they've already tried in addressing their problem and you certainly don't want to be responsible for any duff advice that you may spout.

Your clients already have their own answers. The skill in coaching is to coax the answers out of them through asking challenging questions.

How do I know that the clients already have their own answers? Many a time when I've been foot reading I've listened closely to the questions that a client has asked me and through the way they've worded their question, I've realised the answer that they are looking for.

You probably remember times when you were consulting others about a situation, and you were really pleased when they concurred with what you thought was the right course of action, but when the advice sought didn't match what you thought the correct course of action should be, you carried on asking different people until you heard what you wanted to hear.

Where the answer is not easy to access, reframing the question will often help.

Example of how not to ask questions   2.7.1
I remember the first time I learned this lesson. I was at a Self Actualisation workshop with Mick MacKenzie (see chapter on *Further Information and Recommended Reading*). There was a chap there who had a business idea and he'd expressed that he wanted to find funding for it.

I started saying you could try sourcing a business angel. He explained why that wasn't a solution. Have you tried business link. Yes. Have you….

This continued for some time until Mick interrupted and said, "Jane, what do you want for him?"

"Nothing."

He asked me if I could feel the tension and the rising resistance through my 'suggestions'. And it was true. It had started to feel a bit like an interrogation rather than a helpful suggestion scenario. I guess what I had really wanted was to give the guy a solution. Everything I'd suggested the guy had already investigated.

I was horrified. How many times had I thought that I was being helpful to my clients when I was actually being disrespectful – not taking into account what they'd already tried or what they already knew.

After this experience I started to see how many times I'd start talking about something I was working on, only to have others tell me what to do about it – when in fact, I just wanted to talk it through. Or they'd suggest things to me that I had already considered and rejected. It does tend to irritate.

So from then on, I learned to ask the client what they want, what had they already tried and listen really carefully to what they say so that I can help them to access their own answers rather than telling them what to do.

2.8 Do assume everyone is perfect

When you begin foot reading, assume that your clients are perfect the way they are right now. You are perfect right now. If you knew how to live your life any better, you'd do it.

There isn't a perfect 'foot' to read. We were all born different, with different talents. We all have strengths and weaknesses and often our strengths are also our weaknesses.

For example, there are times when you want someone who has square toe-pads, meaning that they can be stubborn and stick to what they believe doggedly. If they were an activist fighting for a cause you believed in, you'd want them on your side. However, if they believed in the opposite to what you believed, you'd no longer see this stubborn quality as a positive character trait. This is just one example, there are many more. I bet you can think of a few of your own.

We need all the different character types on this planet. When they are working to their full potential their weaknesses become their strengths.

This is why I say that in foot reading, you need to assume that they are perfect the way they are for whatever their life's purpose is.

When you word your foot reading according to this perspective your client will be able to hear the information you are imparting. Would you rather be called 'stubborn' or 'tenacious in the face of opposition'?

Avoid the negative connotations of words and instead choose the more positive phrasing. For example, 'bossy' becomes 'leadership qualities' and 'manipulative' becomes 'ability to get people to do things that you want without them realising it.'

Another way of phrasing a negative is rather than saying the one word, you add the phrase "you have the ability to…" which implies they are not like that all the time and can pick and choose when to do it. So compare:

"You are manipulative," with,
"You have the ability to manipulate."

By using the verb you have changed it from a label to a skill.

2.9   Do make silences work for you

Silence is very powerful. There are times when you are foot reading when you want to fill the silence with your reading. But there are also times when you want to make the silence work for you.

You ask a deep and meaningful question and you receive an initial answer, but by watching the eyes you can see when a person is continuing to think about the question. When this happens, stay silent. Allow them the time and space to continue the thought process without interruption.

By staying out of the way, sometimes the most powerful breakthrough can take place.

2.10   Don't project

You see the world from your own perspective. So in essence, every person you read, to some extent you will be projecting onto them – be it your opinions of right and wrong, your values, or your morals.

Do become much more aware of how you project onto others.

Never tell them what to do because this is so disrespectful. You won't be taking into account what they've already tried, what they like and don't like doing, what their key skills are and who made you the expert all of a sudden?

2.11   Do use projection

OK, so I said 'don't project,' but like all things in life, nothing is black and white. There are times when knowledge of projection can be useful and you can use it as a tool to help understand the client.

There are two ways I use projection:
- Teaching them to understand others in a conflict situation and to stay in their own energy
- Using a card reading.

Let's look at each in turn.

2.11.1
Understanding projection from others
The first way is when they report to me about an incident when they are unfairly accused of something. For example, "He says I'm lazy but I'm not. I'm always helping him, taking care of his needs."

I say, "Who are they talking about, because it's not you."

Explain that everyone projects so if they are saying it about you and it isn't true, then they are probably projecting their own issue onto you.

Before fighting back, ask yourself, 'Who are they talking about?' and if what they accuse you of doesn't sound like you then turn it around and see if it fits them. ("Are you lazy, or is he talking about himself?") It makes it much easier not to be drawn into an argument when you realise this. It's much easier to respond than to react.

I remember when I gave up my office job to take up my career as a full-time foot reader. People said to me, "You'll never earn a living as a foot reader," and I thought, "Who are you talking about? Not me." I realised that they were talking about themselves. They couldn't imagine themselves giving up their day job or earning a living doing foot reading. Fair enough. But it's a good job that I realised they were projecting or I might have listened to them and never taken the leap. Imagine all the fun I would have missed out on by buying into their projection.

Remember, people who are unhappy will try to take your happiness away (maybe not even consciously) and one way they do it is through projection.

> **Example:** I was giving a foot reading in Surrey when Louise told me that she can't keep coasting through life (her facial expression showed she was happy to do just that) and she needed to find a purpose (her facial expression showed lack of interest or energy in this proposal). The incongruity between what she said and how she looked as she was saying it told me that there was more to this. After a bit of questioning, I discovered it stemmed from her daughter asking her how she could bear going through life without a purpose. Until that point Louise had been very contented with her life. Now she was was seeking out this great 'purpose' thing but her heart wasn't really in it because it wasn't something she particularly wanted. She'd been quite happy just doing her own thing. Her daughter was currently leaving school and trying to choose her own path. She was projecting her own stuff onto her Mum. Problem was, her Mum bought into it!

2.11.2   Understanding the client using projection

The second way I use projection is through a card reading. At the beginning of a reading, or at the end of a reading, I often offer the client an inspiration card. These are a selection of cards that have a photograph on one side and an inspirational saying on the other side (made by Your Business Matters Ltd and introduced to me by a friend of mine, Judith Underhill). It's the photograph side that I am interested in using for this exercise. (You can obtain Inspiration Cards from the shop on www.footreading.com or you can make your own.)

The client picks an inspiration card at random and I ask the client to look at the photograph side and read the card meaning to me either literally or metaphorically. I mean by this that they can either describe what they see, or they can tell me what this card means to them symbolically.

Example: When I was teaching in Ely, Cambridgeshire, I offered a card to one of my students. Here's a picture of it so you know what I mean.

I asked the student to describe the card to me. She says, "There's this man at the station." And proceeds to tell a long and involved story about the man. I had to do a double take because I didn't even notice the man standing on the platform. When she concluded the story I asked, "Who on earth are you talking about?"

"My ex-husband," she replied. She had divorced him yet still involved him in her life.

The next student, looking over her shoulder at the card, says, "I don't see that, Jane," so I ask her what she sees. "Fear and loneliness." I do another double take. I don't see that in the photograph either and I realise that she is projecting her situation into the picture.

The third student looks over her shoulder and says, "That's not what I see. I see a train station and the blurry lights indicate that there's lots of movement. It's obviously busy. There's a sign indicating where the train is going but I can't see what it says. There are people. They're going on holiday."

"What? Are you going on holiday this year?"

"No, I'd love to but we can't afford it because we are doing up the kitchen."

So here you see that just from one photograph I've found out information about three different people.

Sometimes just by how they describe the picture you can tell if they are detail oriented or if they focus on the bigger picture. There's a lot you can glean from this exercise.

There's a *Using Cards* section towards the end of this book about how and why I use oracle cards.

2.12 Do listen to the question behind the question

When a client asks you a question, ask yourself what is the energy behind this question? Why are they really asking this question. What is this question revealing about them? Not all questions should be taken at face value.

2.13 As soon as you think you know what is right then you have lost it as a therapist

When someone tells me, "I know why it is. It's because..."

The question I use is:
"Can you think of five other reasons why it might be so?"

There was an experiment done whereby the subjects were asked to view a 30 second piece of film of people playing basketball. They were asked to count the number of ball passes. A few seconds in, a man in a gorilla suit walked onto the court, beat his chest at the camera, and walked off again. Most of the subjects didn't notice. (Source: *Did you spot the gorilla?*, Dr Richard Wiseman, ISBN 9780099466437)

If you are too intent on one thing, you may miss other opportunities and if you think you already have the answer, you block yourself off to all the other possibilities.

Example: At a corporate event, I was greeted in a very croaky voice by our host. He apologised, telling us why he had a croaky voice, blaming it on a virus. When asked "Can you think of five other reasons why you might have a croaky voice?" our host laughed, but humoured us by trying to think up five other reasons. "Maybe it's because we stayed up late last night talking and had to get up early this morning? Maybe it's because we were in a smoky atmosphere? Maybe it's because we've been rehearsing all week? Maybe it's because I'm stressed over organizing this event?" As he started listing the reasons, he opened himself up to finding other solutions to tackling his croaky voice. Was it down to a virus after all?

Example: I had a lady in Cheshire in one of my foot reading seminars. I'd read something on her foot and she started to tell me 'why' it was so. I interrupted her and asked her if she could think of five other reasons why it might be so. She was quite put out not to be allowed to tell her reason, but was soon enjoying thinking up five other reasons, no matter how far-fetched they might be. It opened her up to other possibilities and allowed her to stay curious about other options or opportunities open to her. I explained why I'd asked the question and she went into delight.

The question I used is:

"Can you think of five other reasons why it might be so?"

A lot of energy is wasted in trying to be right all the time. Forget about right or wrong or having to know the answer and stay open to all possibilities.

2.14 Do say what you see but don't draw conclusions

Say what you notice but don't draw conclusions. Noticing is often powerful enough. But drawing a conclusion means you could draw an incorrect conclusion which would undo the good of having noticed something in the first place.

It's easier to show what I mean with an example.

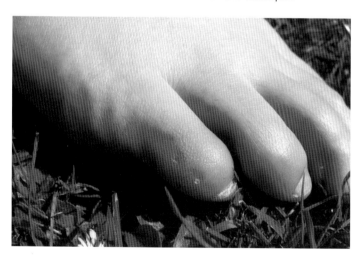

In this photograph there are two corns on the little toe. There are also patches of yellow, red and bruising. To understand what is going on, you need to refer to the emotional map of the foot. Here is a diagram taken from my first book *Let's Read Our Feet!*

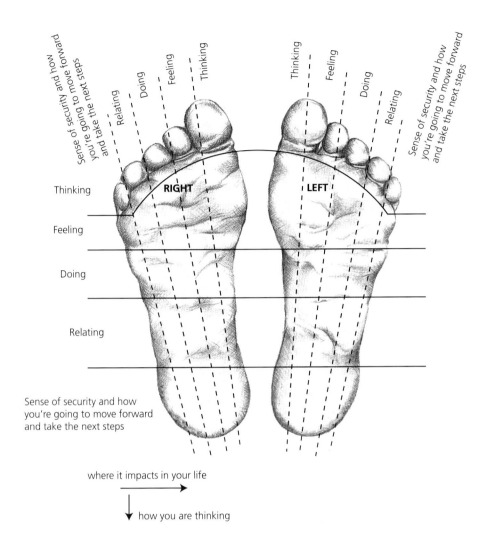

Thinking

Feeling

Doing

Relating

Sense of security and how
you're going to move forward
and take the next steps

where it impacts in your life

how you are thinking

You apply the knowledge that little toe is all about the way you are thinking about your sense of security and how you are going to move forward and take the next step. This is the overview.

But the corns and colours are all showing in a straight line down the fourth zone of the little toe so we can shrink the emotional map of the foot and apply it to the little toe.

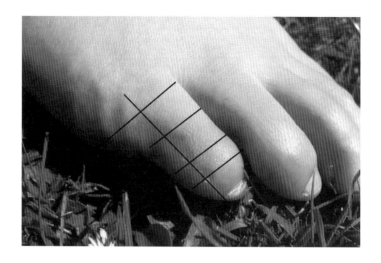

Thus we can see that all the corns and discolouration are showing on vertical zone 4 of the little toe which would represent the way they are thinking about their relationship/private-life/family. So we can conclude that they are protecting themselves over two specific beliefs (corns) concerning their relationship and how it is impacting their emotions and what is being done (zones 2 and 3 horizontally), that they are feeling anger (red) concerning the relationship (zone 4 horizontally), are feeling deep hurt (bruise) concerning the knock to their sense of security and how they are going to move forward and take the next step (zone 5 horizontally) and that they are fed-up (yellow) about protecting their emotions (zone 2 horizontally).

All of this is about a relationship issue because it is in zone 4 vertically on the fifth toe. However, the overall reading is about how they are going to move forward and take the next step because it is on the fifth toe.

So why isn't it on the fourth toe if it's all about relationships? The answer is probably because they are thinking of leaving rather than thinking of staying put and dealing with the relationship. However, what you'd never do is tell the person that they are thinking of leaving. That is drawing a conclusion from the information, rather than just saying what you notice. They may not have arrived at a decision despite the thrust of their thinking. You do not want the responsibility for making their mind up for them. It is enough just to say what you see and not draw a conclusion.

In that way, you are not telling them anything that they don't already know and you are not influencing what the final outcome will be. That's not your decision to make.

That's what I mean about not drawing a conclusion, but just saying what you notice.

Don't pretend to be what you are not 2.15

As a foot reader you often appear to be psychic even though you know you are just reading the structure and blemishes of the foot. Don't pretend to be anything that you are not. Understand your limitations.

You will often be attributed as saying something that you couldn't possibly have known. This is because people often re-interpret what you have said into their situation.

Example: I had a client who had a curved fourth toe right foot. This would indicate hoarding tendencies because they would imbue their objects with memories so when it came time to throw them out, they would find it difficult because it would be like throwing away the memories. However, this particular client did not have an extreme curve, just a slight one, so I probably said something like, "You're not a hoarder, you're a collector".

The next time I saw this client, she said, "Do you remember when you told me that I collected ducks?"

There's no way that I would have known what it was that she collected so I know that I couldn't have said that. This is an example of the client re-interpreting what you say.

2.15.1   Do understand more about fake psychics

I would say that if you are going to become a foot reader, it would be very useful to know more about what charlatan psychics know and do to pass themselves off as psychic because it will help you to understand some of the processes that your clients are going through when they attribute things to you that are not what you said (as I described in the previous example).

Some books that I would recommend with this in mind are the fictional novel *Attack of The Unsinkable Rubber Ducks*, by Christopher Brookmyre (a great story and one that helps to highlight some of the tricks through part of the plot). Also you can read *Tricks of the Mind*, by Derren Brown which has a whole section on Psychics, Mediums and Charlatans. He also has a recommended reading list at the back of his book if you want to read further on the subject.

Because I am a foot reader, I am often mistaken as being psychic and quite often find myself amongst people who claim to be psychic. One time, I'd just finished reading Derren Brown's book only to find someone actually using the same 'psychic' script on me that he quotes in the book. Very annoying.

I'm not saying that all psychics are fakes. They are not. It just helps to know how to spot it and avoid it and how not to fall foul of it yourself. I do believe that if something is 95% improbable, there's still a 5% chance that it is probable. Indeed in 1995, the US Congress asked two independent scientists to assess whether the $20 million that the government had spent on psychic research had produced anything of value. Professor Jessica Utts, a statistician from the University of California discovered that remote viewers were correct 34 per cent of the time, a figure way beyond what chance guessing would allow. She says, "Using the standards applied to any other area of science, you have to conclude that certain psychic phenomena such as remote viewing, have been well established. The results are not due to chance or flaws in the experiments." (Source: *Daily Mail*, 28 Jan 2008)

That figure of 34 per cent would indicate to me that there's still room for maintaining a certain amount of healthy scepticism yet keeping an open mind.

I have, in the past, done foot readings at events where there were psychic readings being offered. If the psychics were too busy I'd get a customer who would have previously chosen a psychic reading. I have to reset their expectations of what the foot reading will yield because I don't read the fortune, the future, or the mind. I read the impact of the emotions and personality on the feet. Then I use coaching skills because I believe everyone already has their own answers. However, I've had great success with helping some of these clients arrive at their own answers and move forward with their problem yet avoiding telling them what to do.

Do know when to back off   2.16

Even when you are right and know you are right about a reading, there are times when you will back off rather than push a point. The person may not be in a space where they are willing or able to hear what you are trying to reveal.

Example of when I had to back off
I was reading a fourth toe right foot that was so curved towards the big toe that when foot reading it could only mean that the person was a hoarder.

"Oh no Love! I've got to stop you there," said the lady.
"You see, me and my daughter, we've been organising."
(At this point I try to stifle a smile because I hear the word
'organising' and understand that it was such a big job that
she needed her daughter's assistance.)

"Really? What have you been organising?" I ask.
"We've organised my shoes and put them all into boxes
and written on the outside what they are."
"And how many pairs of shoes do you have?"
"86."

Eighty-six pairs of shoes, but she's not a hoarder! And then
she continues:
"My daughter said I didn't need that many dinner services
so we've taken some to charity."
"Some? How many dinner services have you left?" I ask.
"Three!"
(My Mum's not even got three and she has a dinner table
that can seat 12!)

So, relative to how she was before, her perception is that
she is not a hoarder. I back off. Yet. I'm imagining the
conversation she has with her daughter when she relates
(indignantly?) how the foot reader accused her of hoarding!

2.17   Do practise!

*"In theory there is no difference between theory and
practice. In practice there is." Yogi Berra, American
Baseball Player.*

If you want to be a good foot reader, you need lots and lots
of practice. The more you practise, the more accurate you
will get, and the more intuitive you will become.

Listen to what your clients say whilst you are doing the reading. If they correct what you say, then listen carefully to the words they use. Often it is just a fine-tuning of the subtle meaning of the words that you originally used. By memorising how they fine-tune your reading, you'll astound the next person by getting it just right.

For example, in the old days I used to say that if they had more than one toe with square toe pads they were stubborn. Until one lady burst out laughing and declared that, "My husband calls me an immovable force!"

It sounds much better to say, "You're an immovable force" because it sounds like a superhero, so I use her words now and every time I say it, it gets a laugh.

Get practising.

Coaching tips, one toe at a time

The next sections of this book show the coaching tips organised by 'toe relevance'.

The assumption made is that you have already read *Let's Read Our Feet!* and already know the meaning of the toes.

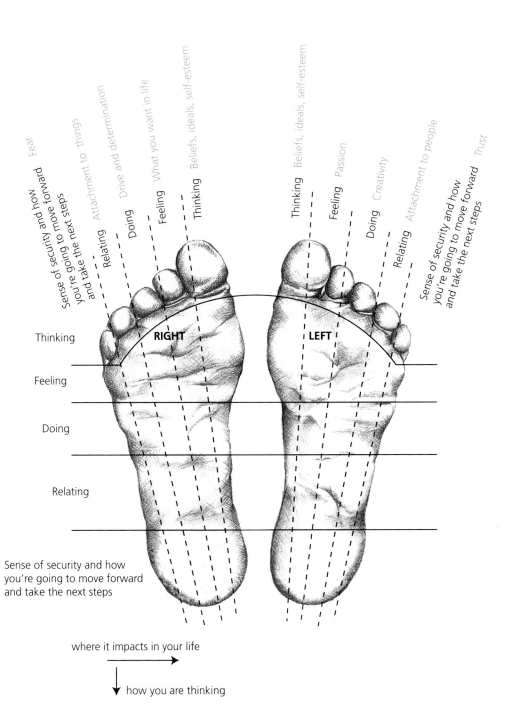

Fear

Sense of security and how you're going to move forward and take the next steps

Relating Attachment to things

Doing Drive and determination

Feeling What you want in life

Thinking Beliefs, ideals, self-esteem

Thinking Beliefs, ideals, self-esteem

Feeling Passion

Doing Creativity

Relating Attachment to people

Sense of security and how you're going to move forward and take the next steps

Trust

Thinking

Feeling

Doing

Relating

RIGHT

LEFT

Sense of security and how you're going to move forward and take the next steps

where it impacts in your life

how you are thinking

Chapter 3
The Big Toe

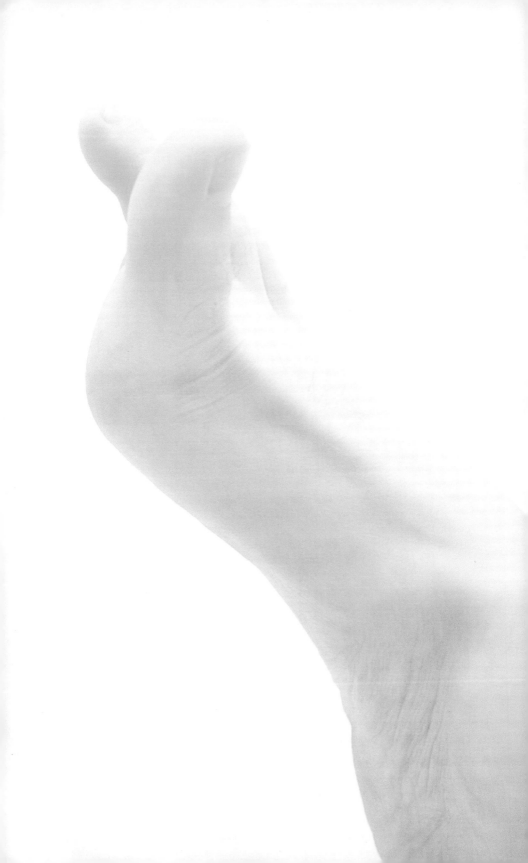

The Big Toe

The big toe represents thoughts, beliefs, ideas and 0, so this section focuses on coaching skills that relate to these areas. The big toe also contains all the energies of the other toes so it is a good guide for getting an overview. Because of this, I've also included details about language and vocalising in this section.

Visualising

When the tip of the toe does not touch the floor because of the toe shape (rather than because the big toe is lifted), as shown in the diagram, then this indicates the ability to visualise. (It would be daydreaming if the big toe were lifted.)

When a client has this toe shape I tell them that this is a fantastic skill to have. They have strong visualisation skills and can picture things in their head in advance. So, for example, it would be the perfect toe shape to have if you are an interior designer. They'd picture the room in their head and know what it would look like finished, even before they put a paintbrush to the wall.

Now the great thing about having this toe shape is that when they harness that visualisation skill, they've got a very powerful tool. If your client has something coming up that they're fearful of, for example if they have to do public speaking, then get them to practise doing it in their head like a movie camera. Visualise doing the public speaking from several different angles, then zooming in so they see the full detail and zooming out from a distance so they can see the bigger picture. Ask them to picture themselves doing it successfully. Picture the audience applauding.

By using this technique, by the time they come to actually do the public speaking, they'll have much more confidence because they'll feel as if they've already done it.

There was an experiment about practising, using three groups where the first group was asked to listen to a piano lesson and then practise the lesson each day for a week. The second group were asked to listen to the piano lesson but then were told to just play anything they liked at their practice sessions for the week. The third group were asked to listen to the piano lesson and then practise the lesson in their head for a week without ever touching a piano. At the end of the week each of the groups were scanned and the conclusion was that there was little difference between the new recorded brain activity in the first and third groups.

Mind your language   3.2

Words are very important. Depending on what language you are using you can massively change the meaning of what you are saying. This was brought home to me when I met a Hawaiian chap and a German chap at a network group.

At the risk of stereotyping, the German language is very precise with definite rules for grammar and precise meanings for words. Hawaiian language is very different as one word can mean as many as ten different things, thus it is not unusual for a conversation in Hawaiian to be conducted on many different levels at once.

For example, when they say 'let's talk story' they are talking not just about telling a story, but also about relating history, whilst acknowledging at the same time that history is never remembered exactly as it was at the time, or they may just be inviting you to have a chat.

When either of these chaps spoke, there was always room for big misunderstandings to occur between them because of their individual understanding of the same language. They both used English to communicate their ideas, yet their mentality was that of their native tongue so very often they may even have been arguing the same point from the same angle, yet enter into a heated discussion because they just couldn't grasp that they were actually agreeing!

As you can see, our language, what is said, what is left unsaid, and what is understood by the other person is very complex. Add into the mix another language, mindset or culture and it gets even more complex. The insights that I'm going to write about here are based on my understanding of the English language through observation of my clients.

3.2.1 Casting Spells

Words have their own power. I believe that we can easily cast spells on each other through our use of language.

When you have a client who looks as though they've been chewing their own toe nails – by that I mean all their toe nails looked ripped or torn and uneven – then you know that they are suffering from negative self-talk.

If they get told that they are useless and can't do anything right, and they hear that message regularly, how long will it be before they start to believe it. Well, it works both ways.

So suggest that next time they hear that little voice in their head being negative, retrain it to say something positive.

If someone says something negative about them, they can try a trick that I've been using for years now. Someone may say something like 'you're so untidy' and I think in my head 'or not'. It's like undoing the spell they are casting! Try it.

Sometimes people say things intending for them to be negative and hurtful and another way of defusing this spell is to say "Thank you for noticing" in a tone that implies that they've just given you the most wonderful compliment.

3.2.2 Missing information

Listen very carefully to the language that is used. Listen not just to what is said, but listen for what is missing.

Listen for generalisations and challenge them:
Client: "Women are emotional."
You: "Which woman specifically? When? In what way?"

Listen for missing information:
Client: "I'm scared."
You: "When? Of what?"

Listen for mistakes in a common phrase or saying.
One day when I was on a workshop observing someone being interviewed – it was a particularly gruelling interview where it felt exhausting just to watch because the interviewee was side-stepping all questions and revealing the absolute minimum. I'd stopped listening out of sheer frustration, but suddenly pricked up my ears when I heard him say, "...it's a bit like throwing the bathwater out with the baby."

The usual phrase is, "...it's a bit like throwing the baby out with the bathwater."

So it really jarred on my ears when I heard it.

I asked whether he had a baby. (Having spent three days with him, this had never been mentioned.) He related how he and his partner had a baby but he couldn't relate to the baby and they split up.

We'd have never obtained this insight if we hadn't noticed the 'slip of the tongue.'

Listen for comparison words (like words ending in 'er' such as bigger, smaller etc.) and understand what the comparison criteria were:
Client: "She is better for me."
You: "Better than what?"

Listen for examples of mind-reading!
Client: "He/she never considers my feelings."
You: "How do you know he/she never considers your feelings?" Or, "what feelings specifically?"
(Here also the word 'never' is also a giveaway. Listen for superlatives and challenge them too.)

Listen for super powers! You're a human being with your own mind, body, and free will. So listen out for phrases that begin with 'He or she makes me...'

Client: "She makes me angry."
You: "How specifically does she 'make' you angry?"

(Can anyone 'make' you do anything? What is it about a given situation that you allow yourself to become <insert emotion>.)

Client: "She never considers my feelings."
You: "How do you know that she never considers your feelings?"
Client: "Because she stays out so late every night."
You: "Does her staying out late every night always mean that she never considers your feelings?"

You can understand a lot about a person's view of the world if you listen out for the words:
Good, bad, crazy, sick, correct, right, wrong, only, true, false. E.g. there's *only* one way to peel an orange. It's *wrong* to hurt anyone's feelings.

Try adding the words 'for me' into the sentence and you get a clearer view of their world. "There's only one way for me to peel an orange." "It's wrong for me to hurt anyone's feelings."

As a foot reader, your own use of language has to be precise. Avoid using the terms right, wrong, good or bad and thus avoid appearing judgemental. Things are what they are and you have to accept that the person is doing the best that they can with the information that they have right now. You view the world from your perspective; allow them to view it from theirs.

Challenge generalisations:
Client: "They never do anything for me."
You: "They NEVER do ANYTHING for you?"

Having told you about how to listen for missing information, I'd like to share with you a few instances where I'd gleaned more information using these methods in conjunction with Doreen Virtue's *Healing with the Fairies* oracle cards, published by Hay House. (There's more about how and why I use these cards in section 9.)

Story about a client who revealed their thoughts through their words 3.2.3

George had picked the card 'Parenting and Children' but despite the fact he was married with children, he couldn't resonate with the information about the card. I'm used to working with the cards and I can usually tell when they've picked the right card for them. My intuition told me it was the right card for him, even if he couldn't resonate with it. I decided to let him pick another card from a different pack but this time asked him to hold a specific question in mind. He still didn't resonate with the card chosen. I asked him if he minded telling me his question. It was, "Where will I be in five years time…um…you know, my family".

The way he phrased it, the intonation and the fact he'd picked 'parenting and children' earlier and not resonated with it made me ask, "Are you thinking about leaving?" He was.

Story about a client who revealed their thoughts through their words 3.2.4

Again I had been using Doreen Virtue's *Healing with the Fairies* oracle cards (see section 9). This time, Fiona had picked the card for 'Kindness'. I read to her the meaning of the card. When I got to the words "practise this kindness habit daily and you will soon attract new loving friends into your life," she reacted as if I'd slapped her and she exclaimed, "Even men?"

I ignored the reaction until I got to the end of the reading. As I set the cards aside, I said, "Who is he, and I don't mean your husband," so she told me all about her situation.

I picked up on her reaction because usually the words 'attract new loving friends into your life' makes people think of friendships, so her reaction told me there was something else happening here.

Criticism or feedback?

Don't you hate being told what to do? Don't you find it difficult to listen when someone implies that you are wrong, they are right and they start the age-old 'what you want to do is...' conversation? Even the best feedback won't be heard if it's delivered with any kind of judgement or criticism.

Feedback is very useful. Criticism is not very useful. There's a big difference between feedback and criticism. Say what you observe, factually, avoiding all judgemental language.

As children, we often get feedback both positive and negative. We get told when we are doing well, how beautiful our 'birds nest' drawings are and how helpful we are. We get told when we are in trouble, when we've broken a rule, when we've made a mistake.

As adults, we rarely get positive feedback. I make it a point when I'm doing a foot reading to point out the things that the person is doing well and the positive differences shown when comparing the past foot to the present foot.

It's also useful when doing a hands-on treatment to note what the person looks like on arrival and then to tell them physiologically how different they look on departure. This allows their subconscious mind to absorb and work on it.

In fact, when I am noting the physiological impact I avoid the use of words such as positive and negative, good and bad, and focus instead on accurate, factual, physiological detail spoken without judgemental words.

When teaching foot reading, I often remind my class how tentative they were at the beginning of the practical session and how much more confidently they deliver their messages by the end of the session.

When doing reflexology, I remind the client of what they originally requested and how far they have progressed.

So, when foot reading, remember to offer praise to the client where you can see improvements from the past foot to the present foot (right versus left) and in giving an accurate foot reading, they can enjoy the positive feedback.

Doing too much for others 3.4

'If you spend time, what do you buy? Less Time.'
Mrs Baxter in Kate Atkinson's Human Croquet

If a client has a bunion or if the angle of the big toe is leaning towards the little toe, then this means that they are either (when at a slight angle) motivated by helping others or (when at an acute angle) are bending over backwards doing far too much for others and not enough for themselves.

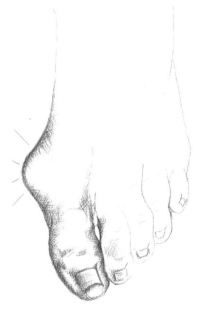

When you see this, you ask them, "If you had more time for you, what would you do with it?"

Usually they don't know, so ask, "I know you don't know, but if you did know, what might it be?"

Sounds like the same question but is worded in such a way to allow them permission not to know, but also allow them to get curious.

Often the client will tell you that they would spend their spare time doing something for someone else, which defeats the object of the question, so remind them that the question was about spending time for them to help them to re-energise.

The reason why you are asking this question is so that if they can identify how they would like to spend time on themselves to re-energise and rebalance then they will have a good reason to learn to say 'No' more often and to guard some time and space for themselves.

Once you've helped them to identify one thing that they would do to help themselves to get back into balance, then ask them to get their diary out and schedule it into their timetable.

Explain that it is not wrong to do things for others, but if you are doing far too much you will experience burn-out and then be no good to anyone, so by keeping the balance right you will be able to continue to help people.

3.4.1   On saying 'No'

One of the hardest things for a person who has spent a lifetime bending over backwards doing too much for others, is saying 'No'.

I suggest to them that they start with the small things like instead of jumping up to make a cup of tea, they say, "Do you know? I'd really like someone to make me a cup of tea this time." Then build up to more important things once they've practised on the little stuff.

When teaching this in Australia, one of my students taught me her mantra:
"Every time I say 'No' I say 'Yes' to myself."

Swollen necks of big toes   3.4.2
Sometimes you'll notice a deep line or crease at the joint above the neck of the big toe. This often occurs when the neck of the big toe is swollen.

Necks of toes represent expression. If the necks of the big toes are swollen then they aren't saying what they need to say. Usually it is because they worry what everyone else thinks.

I used to have this problem until my friend Simon reframed it for me. He said, *"Every minute of every day, you teach people how to treat you. So by saying nothing, you're teaching them that it is OK, when it's not."*

Oh my goodness. When you put it like that, all of a sudden you realise that you have responsibility for yourself and it's up to you to teach people how to treat you. It makes it much easier to say what you need to say.

I recently received an email saying, *"I have been thinking of you lots this Christmas and the impact your visit has had on me personally. It is hard to believe that the phrase 'teach people how to treat you' could have had such a profound effect. Thank you..."*

3.4.3 **Example:** On one of my overseas trips, I suspected that someone who was helping me was also stealing from me. I had the usual spiral of thoughts along the lines of "Oh no, I can't accuse them of stealing. What if I'm wrong? I'd feel awful. Maybe I should just wait until I'm sure. Is there another explanation? How can I be sure?" You can imagine – a whole spiral of self-doubt and a wish to avoid conflict.

Then I remembered, "Every minute of every day, you teach people how to treat you, so by saying nothing, you're teaching them that it is OK."

That little sentence changed everything for me. I realised that even if I wasn't absolutely sure about the facts, I had to teach this person that it was not OK with me if someone was stealing. I waited until they handed over the money from some sales they were doing for me and I said, "There's not enough money here."
"Are you sure?"
"Yes."
And the person handed over the rest of the money. That was it. And in that moment we both knew where we stood. That person knew that I had noticed and I knew that my suspicion was correct. Everything changed from that point.

Let me assure you that with practice it gets easier and easier too.

This story also reminds me to say that if you want a magnificent life you have to surround yourself with magnificent people!

3.4.4 **Time management**
Tied in with the bunion toe and not having enough time, you'll also want to offer some tips on time management. Time Management information is also suitable for people with toes leaning towards the little toe. That would mean

that the energy of that toe is in a rush for the future, not being in the moment.

- Look at where you spend your time
- Look at your goals
- Avoid multi-tasking
- Do the important things first
- Check email on a schedule
- Know your best time to work, rest and play
- Make it easy to get started.

Look at where you spend your time

3.4.4.1

Before the client does anything about their time management, get them to keep a short diary for a week of how they are spending their time so that they can analyse it. I've tried this before and it's rather surprising to see the difference between how you think you spend your time and how you actually spend it! For example, when I have a creative project, I spend more time procrastinating by doing non-important tasks than I do in actually tackling the project. Now I overcome that by having a specific start and end time and discipline myself to stick to it.

Look at your goals

3.4.4.2

When your client has finished recording their time for the week, then ask them to write a list of their goals. Ask them to take time assessing what is important. The actual content of their goals doesn't matter so long as they are meaningful to them and can help them look at the bigger picture. (You don't want to get bogged down with to-do lists when the items on that list don't relate to your overall goals.)

Now, ask them to compare their list of goals with how they have been spending their time. How much of their time is spent doing things that take them away from their goals?

Don't forget that goals can also include 'having fun'. Sadly the corporate world seems to have hijacked the idea of goal setting. Let's bring it back to including some of the important things in life like fun, rest, laughter, eating etc.

Areas to consider when setting goals:
- Home Life
- Relationship
- Work Life
- Play and Fun
- Learning
- Finance
- Once-in-a-lifetime Idea.

3.4.4.3 Avoid multi-tasking
Multi-tasking has its place and is a very positive skill. But when people are overloaded and stressed and time is critical, multi-tasking might make us feel as though we are achieving lots, but it stops us from enjoying it whilst we are doing it and may even pull us off that critical task. When time is really short we can end up starting lots and finishing nothing, so to get that feeling of having accomplished something, focus on one thing at a time.

Does it matter if you've done the hoovering whilst loading the washer whilst boiling the eggs, if you've not paid the credit card bill on time?

Suggest to your client to focus on the important things rather than the volume of what they are getting done and in giving it their full attention – who knows, they may even enjoy getting it done.

3.4.4.4 Do the important things first
Suggest setting aside an hour a day to tackle those important jobs. By setting a time, they won't be able to get away with procrastinating.

Check email on a schedule   3.4.4.5

In this day and age I'd be mad to ignore the effect of emails on time management. Suggest setting a specific time to check and reply to emails rather than checking them as soon as they come in. In this way, they are able to focus on what they are doing rather than letting the email dictate how they spend their time.

I have different email addresses for different things so, for example, I can prioritise checking book orders before I go to the post office by just checking that specific email inbox.

Even though I work from home I have separate emails for work and for personal stuff.

I also use folders in my inbox to help cut out the time I spend looking for old emails and to keep track of emails pending a response.

If you feel as though you are controlling your email rather than your email controlling you then email can be fun.

Know your best time to work, rest and play   3.4.4.6

Referring back to your client's analysis of how they spend their time, you'll begin to see trends. Note the times when they work best and most productively.

If, like me, they have an afternoon slump, then they can allocate that as the time to rest or to play.

Ever watched a cat have a mad half hour? Let's advocate one for ourselves so we can let off a bit of steam!

Some people work best at night, preferring that time when most people are asleep because they are least likely to be disturbed. Others prefer to do their work first thing in the morning (freaks!). Guess which I prefer!

I find that I am more creative after a walk. So when I am writing, I prepare my writing plan, then go for a walk, using the time to muse and when I get back I find I'm better able to settle down into my writing. Plus it makes me feel good.

One of my clients wanted to study for her forthcoming exams but was getting very frustrated about the lack of time that she had for such study. On analysis of how she spent her time, we discovered that the seven hours that she spent in her car could be used to play back audio tapes related to her subject. She got so into this that she had her husband making recordings of him reading her notes! She also got up 45 minutes earlier each day to add some extra study time.

3.4.4.7   Make it easy to get started

In the past when I had to do any creative work, I used to do everything else first. All those silly time-wasting jobs that never get done, would suddenly grab my attention and I simply must do them before I start my creativity. Getting started is the hardest thing. Once you've started, you get so absorbed and it soon gets done. So make it easy to get started.

If it's housework you avoid, make it easier to start by having the cleaning products in the area that needs doing. Buy a bottle of product for each area if it helps.

If it's writing you find difficult, set aside an area already geared up, with paper, pens, dictionary, thesaurus, stamps, calculator so all you have to do is sit down at that place and get started.

In January I always have a clutter clearing session. I'd avoided doing my bookcase for a few years in a row and this particular year I was determined to do it. I spent a few days just looking at it and feeling daunted by the idea.

Remembering that if you make it easier to get started you're more likely to tackle something – the night before my day off, I pulled all the books out of the bookcase and dumped them on the floor then went to bed. I hate mess, so when I got up the next day it was much easier to get started on the task! I ended up taking two bin bags of books to the charity shop that day.

Whatever it is, you get the idea – make it easier to get started.

_____

And for further reading about time management I suggest the book *Do it tomorrow and other secrets of time management*, by Mark Forster.

Chapter 4
The Second Toe

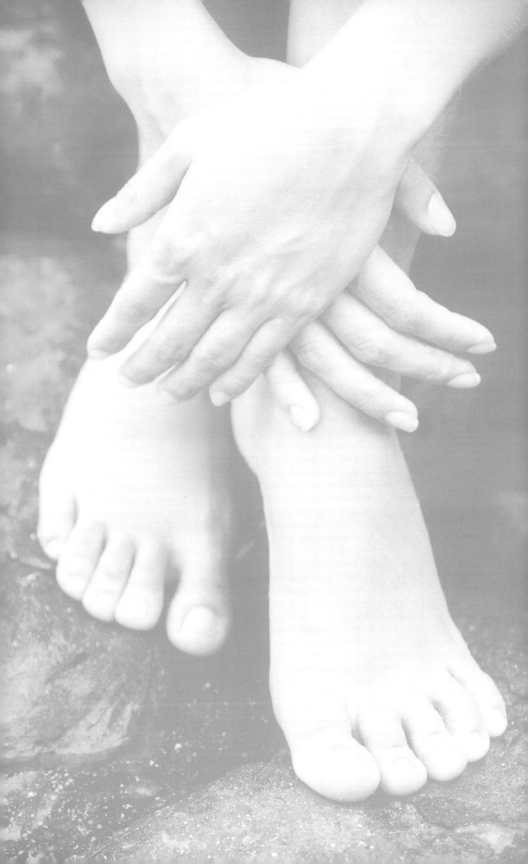

The Second Toe

The general meanings of the second toes are about emotions and feelings. When reading the nuance differences, the second toe on the right foot is about what you want in life and the second toe on the left foot is about your passion in life.

Empathy   4.1

Anyone in a highly emotional state needs to know that they are being heard and are understood. When a client is telling you how they are feeling, reflect it back at them.

Engaging into a conversation about the 'rights' and 'wrongs' of a situation is not going to help. Remember the end goal is to coach the client towards a solution that will unblock their situation.

Reflect back how they feel so that they know you have understood what they are trying to express. When they've finished expressing themselves, don't try to fix it for them. You are not in their situation. You don't know what is best for them. They already have their own answers – remember your role is to assist them in finding their answers.

The affirmation, "I don't know how I created this situation in my life. I'm sorry and I love you," is a very powerful affirmation and it allows you to move the client away from the rights and wrongs of a situation to help it to heal.

Listen. Empathy involves listening more than it involves regaling your client with all your own trials and tribulations! This is about them and not about you.

4.2   What do you want in life?

Second toes of both feet ungrounded – not touching the floor – mean that you don't know what you want to be when you grow up! Second toe right foot represents what you want in life and second toe left foot represents your passion in life. So if they are both not touching the floor those energies are not grounded. I'd read it as, "You don't know what you want to be when you grow up!" They've lost their way and are not connected to their passion in life.

As soon as I see second toes ungrounded, I switch into coaching with the question, "If you only have seven days to live and you knew it and anything were possible, even magic, what would you do, be or create?"

It's a powerful question and one I use a lot with my clients. Their first reaction is usually "I don't know."
"I know you don't know, but if you did know, what might it be?"
Then they may tell me what they don't want.

It goes something like this:

"If you only had seven days to live and you knew it, and anything were possible (even magic), what would you do, be or create?"

"I don't know."

"I know you don't know, but if you did know, what might it be?"

And then I can watch as their curiosity is aroused. It sounds like the same question but saying "I know you don't know" allows them not to know and saying "If you did know, what might it be" allows them to explore the possibilities.

Usually, then they will tell you what it is they don't want.

"Well, I wouldn't go to work!"

The brain is like a small child. You yell, "Don't touch that glass!" and the child touches it. You say, "Careful, don't spill it" and what happens? The brain doesn't hear the word 'Don't'.

Don't think of a pink elephant in a blue spotted cardigan. Oops! Too late!

They said, "Well, I wouldn't go to work!"

See the answer? With this focus on what they don't want, their brain is telling them to go to work. It's counter-productive. By focusing on what they don't want, they're getting more of it.

If you focus on a negative, you tend to get more of it. The brain works that way.

So, thinking about my clients, as soon as they say what they don't want, I point this out to them, and get them to focus on what they do want.

"Okay, so you wouldn't want to go to work. That's what you don't want. What do you want?"

It seems like such a tiny difference, yet it's such a powerful difference. Like the old saying, 'the devil is in the detail!'

Very occasionally the reverse of this happens. There are times when the client tells me what they don't want and it is exactly what they do want!

Example: I had a client in San Diego who replied, "Well I wouldn't want to travel because I've already done that, and I wouldn't want to be with my friends," so I rephrased what she said as a question. "If you could travel anywhere with your friends, what would you do?" And without skipping a beat she said, "I'd take them to play all the golf courses around Europe, starting with St Andrews." She hadn't noticed that this was exactly what she said she didn't want, nor had she noticed I'd rephrased what she said she didn't want as a question.

Wait a minute. How do you know when the client is telling you what they don't want, and it's really what they do want? How did I know in the example above to break the usual rule and assume it was the reverse?

Simple. It's through observation. I often watch the face when I ask a question to see whether the person 'lights up' when they reply. Even though this lady was telling me what she didn't want, she seemed to 'light up' as she was telling me.

Remember, people are paradoxes and some are very good at keeping the truth from themselves.

Be prepared that when you ask the question, *"If you only had seven days to live and you knew it, and anything were possible (even magic), what would you do, be or create?"* there will be an emotional reaction to the question.

There's no point pushing on with the questioning without first releasing the emotion. Acknowledge that you've noticed the emotional reaction. Then follow with the technique for releasing old emotions described in the next section.

Once you've assisted the client to clear the emotion, the client is ready for you to continue.

Ask the question again.
"If you only had seven days to live and you knew it, and anything were possible (even magic), what would you do, be or create?"

It's not important what the answers are. It's important that the person becomes **curious** about what the answers might be. They will be thinking about the question long after they leave you.

When they give me answers, the first few they give me I tend to disregard. They often tell me what they think I want to hear, or what they think the 'right' answer will be. There is no right answer. How would I know what might be fun for them or what they should do with their life? All I'm interested in is that they get curious about it and start looking for their own answers.

If when they answer me, they 'light up' and their response has energy and impact, then I may very well believe them and work further with them on how to achieve the idea they've hit upon.

The key is **curiosity**. This is one of the highest states you can be in, and from curiosity, change can occur.

One of my friends, Sylvia Ferguson, is a reflexologist and she told me about how someone I had coached was very worried that they only had seven days to live. Eek! That wasn't my intention. So now I am very careful to finish the session off by telling them that I don't know how long they have and neither does anyone.

Your life is happening right now, not some time in the future and the point is to live it right now. Wasn't it John Lennon who said, "Life is what happens to you when you're busy doing something else."

Viktor Frankl wrote the book *Man's Search for Meaning* which I urge you to read. From this, he developed Logotherapy. He was a psychiatrist who was able to view first hand in a concentration camp just how powerful the human spirit is when that person has a meaning to their life.

What questions can you ask your client to help them rediscover their meaning and purpose in life?

Questions I find useful are:
- *What do you want?*
  How many times do we ever get asked what do we want? It can be a very impactful question.
- *What result would you love to create?*
- *What is fun for you?*
  This is a real killer of a question. Most people aren't having very much fun and to ask that question makes them realise it. Be prepared to clear the rising emotions before you can continue with this one.
- *What is it that, when you are doing it, time stands still for you?* This question is all about being in the flow – when you find that thing that so engrosses you, you could spend all day doing it and feel like only five minutes has gone by. If you can find out what that is for you and manage to get paid for it you'll never work another day in your life!
- *When you had the school holidays stretching out in front of you, how did you spend your time?*
  This is a great one to ask if life has got in the way and

the client has lost all sense of what is fun for them. In an average upbringing, most kids did things that were fun for them. However, don't ask this question if the person has a little toe that is very short compared to the other toes. If this is the case, they had to grow up too quickly and you won't be doing them any favours by making them dwell on it.

Another technique I like to use is, once the person has worked out their aims, to ask the person to imagine they are meeting themselves in five years time. Imagine the five years older person telling you what they've achieved and how they've done it and suggest what one change they can make today to help get themselves on track.

Releasing old emotions   4.2.1

Giving a foot reading carries a certain responsibility. Sometimes you are saying what you see, but the person whose feet you are reading has been hiding their feelings, or it is the first time they are hearing what they are feeling being said out loud. It can be quite an emotional time for them and sometimes you will have a client who reacts with tears. So how do you deal with this?

It's useful to have a technique designed to release old emotions. I'll summarise the technique at the end of this section so that you can copy the technique and keep it close by when you are working.

Normally when you see someone crying, you want to offer them a tissue, or give them a hug or pat their hand or some other such intrusion. However, this interrupts their body's ability to release what they are feeling.

As soon as you see the client having an emotional reaction, stop what you are doing and say something along the lines of… "I can see you are feeling emotional. Please shut your eyes and go into your body and point to where you are feeling the emotion." They will then point to where the emotion is welling up. I deliberately ask them to point rather than to talk at this stage, because if they're anything like me, when I get upset and am asked to talk, it comes out as a squeak.

Next, ask them what colour it is and tell them to take their time. It does sound a bit strange, but invariably they do see a colour or colours. Once they have taken time to connect with what colour it is, ask them what shape it is. Some people see a geometric shape and others see a whole animation in all its technicolour glory. It doesn't matter.

Ask them what texture it is. Is it rough, jagged, fluffy, smooth, diffused?

Then I ask them to breathe in white light and breathe out the colour they first saw. If they didn't see a colour I just say, "Breathe in white light and release." They do the breathing thing three times. Then I ask, "Do you feel the same or different?" Depending on their answer, I may go round a second time, or I will stop as the work is done.

I would like to stress that it is very important not to attach any reason or meaning to the sensations that they are having. Don't interpret. It is the mere fact that they are observing and getting curious about their body's sensations that is helping them to release the feelings quicker. If you attach a reason to it, it will stay around for longer. The aim here is to release.

Time and time again I have seen this method work incredibly well. It does go against the natural instinct, to hold back and not offer comfort to the client, but to be honest, as soon as you start asking them these questions, their tears tend to dry up as they get curious about themselves.

Once they have tried this technique, you can encourage them to repeat the technique any time they feel emotional in order to help them to release it quickly and efficiently.

I've had clients who feel it in their throat, or heart, or stomach. I've had them see just one colour, or see several colours. You can always tell the artists amongst us because they are extremely precise about the colour they are seeing. It's not just 'red' it's 'scarlet vermillion!' I've had some just seeing one simple shape, or some seeing complex shapes like keyholes or head and shoulders. Sometimes the colours change as they focus on them. Sometimes they break up and move to another area.

If the colours they see are swirling, I sometimes ask them to move it to an inch away from their body, to slow down the swirling, then to make it swirl in the other direction. Once they see they have control over it, I ask them to blow it away.

The emotional release technique summarised   4.2.2

- From where in your body do you feel the emotion welling up?
- What colour is it?
- What shape is it?
- What texture is it?
- Breathe in white light and breathe out the colour (three times)
- Do you feel the same or different now?

If there is some residual emotion, go round again.

4.3   Leadership

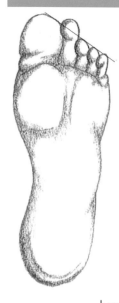

If you drew a line across the majority of the toes, and the second toe was over that line, then this would indicate strong leadership qualities.

If the person is not in a leadership role then they can become bossy!

If the person you are reading has not yet got themselves in a leadership role, then it is worth encouraging them to explore this side of their nature.

When I am teaching, if I have a few people in my class with this type of toe then I allocate them 'monitor' roles. I give them something to be in charge of, such as overseeing the air-conditioning or collecting the lunch orders. In this way, they are using their leadership abilities usefully and not trying to take over my class!

If both the second and the third toe are over the line then it's very important that you help them to understand the quality of the third toe over the line.

Third toe over the line means that the person has so much drive and determination that they can do twice what the next person can do given the same time and resources. It's a blessing and a curse! This means that when they delegate they can get very frustrated because the other person can't do half what they can do!

Couple this talent for doing twice as much as the next person, with the leadership qualities and you can have quite a potent combination.

In Hawaii I was watching the feet of people queuing in *Joy's Place* café. I asked a lady, "Excuse me, do you mind my asking, are you a manager?" To which she replied "Yes, I am. How do you know that?" and I explained about the long second toe. She added, "I used to own my own business," and I interrupted her, saying I bet I can tell you why you got rid of it. I pointed to her third toe over the line and explained about how frustrated she would get when delegating because they could not do half of what she could do given the same time and resources. She agreed that this was the case. She admitted that she still got frustrated even now with people not doing what she'd expected in a given timeframe.

So you can see why I say the combination of the second toe and third toe being over the line can be quite a potent combination. They need to learn that this ability to do twice as much as the next person is their talent and they need to learn that when delegating they should let the next person have twice as much time and resources.

Narrow to wide toe 4.4

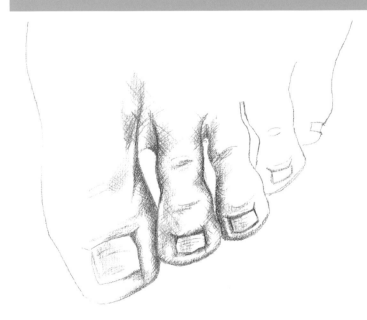

A second toe that is shaped narrow at the base then widens at the tip indicates that the person is a bit of a drama queen!

What I mean is that whatever emotion they are feeling, the person on the receiving end experiences it in an over-exaggerated manner.

So if they are feeling slightly irked, the other person will perceive them as being really angry.

It's great when they are in a good mood but not so great when they are in a bad mood!

By making them more aware of their impact on others, they can choose whether they're happy with that or wish to change.

4.5   Wide to narrow

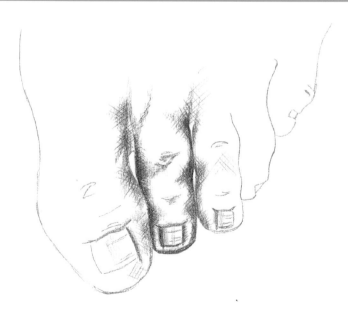

A second toe that is wider at the base (where it joins the foot) than at the tip, indicates that this person compromises too much.

Why? It's not serving you well.

Sometimes this tendency to over-compromise can stem from feelings of inadequacy, low self-confidence or a wish to avoid conflict.

Ask the client to observe when and why they are compromising then help them to develop a strategy to stand firm.

It's not wrong to compromise unless it's always one way.

Rituals   4.6

Sometimes, to help release an old emotion, a ritual is required.

There are already many forms of formalised rituals in our society, the most common being those for Weddings and Funerals. Sometimes society hasn't got a formalised ritual suitable for our needs.

I've been noticing through my clients that when a miscarriage occurs, the grieving has no obvious outlet. This is one example where a ritual to mark the event can be very healing. Sometimes they plant a tree. Sometimes they wear a piece of jewellery to remind them (not as a reminder of a negative occurrence but to mark the miracle of that conception, however brief). Sometimes they light a candle and read a prayer or a letter that they have composed themselves for the occasion.

I know someone who needed to forgive a parent with whom she no longer had any contact. As it was impossible for her to say all she needed to say to them in person, we devised a ritual whereby she said her forgiveness silently, then symbolically released a helium balloon to represent her burden being lifted and letting go of the situation.

Without revealing who it was, or going into too much detail, perhaps by reading these extracts of thank you letters I received you can understand how effective a simple ritual can be.

"Thank you so much for my wonderful and enlightening foot reading. I came away feeling amazingly positive. I have said goodbye to X with a helium balloon. I am no longer 'hitting myself on the head with a hammer!"

"I burned a candle and a letter for my miscarriage. It feels as though a huge weight has been lifted. Thanks again."

In a situation where we have feelings of being out of control, allowing a feeling of control, or taking action can make a big difference.

4.7   Feeling Blue

Human brains seem to be naturally endowed with the need to exercise control, be effective, change things, influence things, make things happen. Take away the opportunity to do that and you leave a person depressed.

I've noticed a high incidence of depression at apparently wealthy places. They seem to have everything – swimming pool, big house, expensive car, lots of friends – yet also depression.

I decided at the time that depression seems to stem from not getting what you want in life and losing control. The thing these people all had in common is that they perceived they had too much to lose if they changed the direction of their life. They felt they couldn't possibly change and this brought on the feelings of depression. (Depression shows on the feet as black-coloured toe pads.)

Obviously it's not the only reason for depression. Yet, as often happens when I'm trying to work something out, I came across an article by Daniel Gilbert (referencing the following three studies: M.E.P. Seligman, *Helplessness: On Depression, Development, and Death* (San Francisco: Freeman, 1975) and E. Langer and J. Rodin, 'The Effect of Choice and Enhanced Personal Responsibility for the Aged: A Field Experiment in an Institutional Setting', *Journal of Personality and Social Psychology* 34:191–98 (1976) and J. Rodin and E.J. Langer, 'Long-Term Effects of a Control-Relevant Intervention with the Institutional Aged', *Journal of Personality and Social Psychology* 35:897–902 (1977).

Daniel Gilbert says human beings come into the world with a passion for control, they go out of the world the same way, and research suggests that if they lose their ability to control things at any point between their entrance and their exit, they become unhappy, helpless, hopeless and depressed.

In one study researchers gave elderly residents in a nursing home a plant. For the high-control group (i.e. the group given more control) they told the residents they could water and feed and take care of the plant themselves. For the low-control group (i.e. the group given less control) they told them that the staff would tend to the plant. Six months later 30% of the low-control group had died as opposed to 15% of people in the high-control group.

A follow-up study confirmed the importance of perceived control for the welfare of nursing-home residents but had an unexpected and unfortunate end. This time the high-control group were allowed to control timing and duration of the student volunteers' visits. The low-control group were told by the student volunteer when the visit would take place and for how long. After two months, residents in the high-control group were happier, healthier, more active and taking fewer medications than those in the low-control group. At this point the researchers concluded their study and discontinued the student visits. Several months later they learned that a disproportionate number of residents who had been in the high control group had died. Only in retrospect did the cause of this tragedy seem clear. Apparently, gaining control can have a positive impact on one's health and well-being, but losing control can be worse than never having had any at all.

Hence, this is why I offer a ritual to someone in situations where they feel they have no control, to allow them to take back control of their life, no matter in how small a way.

With people who are depressed, I teach them the emotional release technique to show them that they are not the same from minute to minute.

I ask them what they really want. Keeping communication open helps.

It is best to refer them to a specialist. Sometimes the chemical imbalance needs balancing before any other therapies can help. Treatment is usually with anti-depressant drugs, cognitive behavioural therapy or psychotherapy. Yet Patrick Holford, co-author of *Food is Better Medicine than Drugs* suggests a nutritional approach for someone with a-typical depression. An a-typical depression would be found in someone who is tired all the time, gains weight, has mood swings.

In a trial chromium was given to a-typical depression sufferers. The result was a two third drop in the number of sufferers and a 60% drop in remission rates. Within 30 minutes of taking chromium the mood improves.

Omega 3 is also useful. Six out of eight depression sufferers given Omega 3 showed significant signs of improvement, double the numbers seen for those taking SSRI antidepressants (which double the risk of suicide). The best results were with 1000mg of EPA.

5-HTP is great for treatment in depression. It causes a reduction in appetite and an improvement in mood. It works on serotonin levels. There is, however, a contra-indication. Don't take 5-HTP when you are on anti-depressants. Start it as you come off the drug. Patrick's launching a book on *New Optimum Nutrition for the Mind* in October 2008. In the meantime, you may want to contact the Brain Bio Centre in Richmond, Greater London, for help.

In colour therapy, the colour magenta is associated with compassion and nurturing and I've noticed that women suffering from depression tend to be drawn to the colour magenta and often wear it on their toe nails.

Gratitude   4.8

Helping a client to change their attitude is not an easy thing to do. If they have a 'glass is half empty' attitude and would like to change it, then here's a technique they could try.

Buy a notebook and each day they are to write a list of things from that day that they are thankful for. They aren't allowed to write anything that does not fit the category of being thankful or showing gratitude.

Some days, they'll write long lists and other days it will be a real struggle to think of anything. When this happens ask them to take a good look around them at the things in their room as they write. Have they got electricity? Be thankful that they have.

After a week of this, they can look back at the lists they have made each day and start to see all the things they have to be thankful for. Each day they know they'll have to be writing their new list so they are actively looking for things to write on their list. It changes their focus and creates a new behaviour.

It doesn't just have to be used for gratitude either, this technique can be used for a number of other focuses that you'd like to introduce. The key here is that the client is interested in change.

Chapter 5
The Third Toe

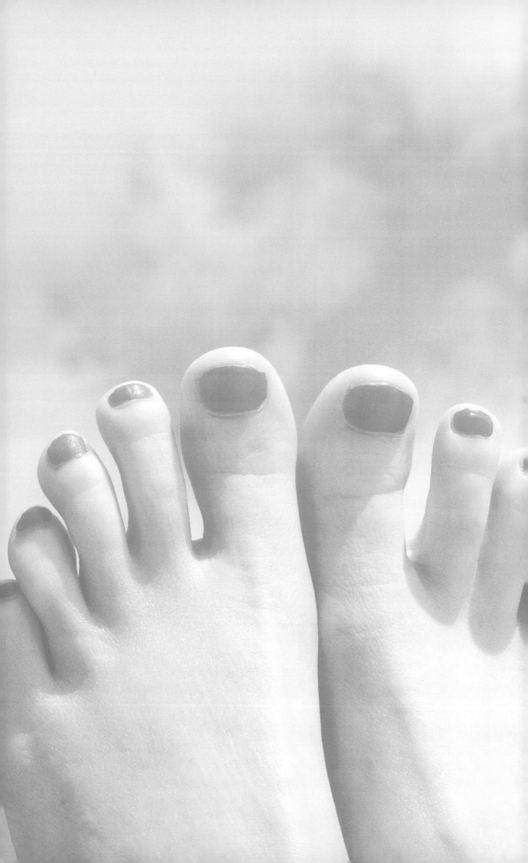

The Third Toe

The third toe is all about doing – chores, work, job, career, action. Third toe right foot is about drive and determination and third toe left foot is all about creativity. In my first book *Let's Read Our Feet!* I described the third toe right foot as representing 'aggression' but over time and with experience I've changed my mind and believe that 'drive and determination' is a more accurate description.

Ambition   5.1

What are your ambitions? Do you have any? Have you ever written them down? Surveys show that if you write down your goals you are more likely to achieve them.

Focus more on your goals rather than on your 'to do' list. It's very easy to get pulled off track unless you have a sense of where you are heading.

If you already know what you want to be doing, find yourself a mentor. Remember that as your skills improve, you may need to find a new mentor in line with your new skills.

Model success. Study who did what you want to do and how, but add your own passion. Inspire others to get what you want.

Ambitions don't just have to be about work either. I have a friend who loves bird-watching and has so focused his life on this hobby that it even dictates what jobs he takes, choosing only those where it wouldn't matter if he took a day off at a moment's notice to be able to follow a migrating bird blown off course into our country.

5.2   Third toes not touching the floor

If the third toes are not touching the floor then the person is off-track career-wise. You could suggest career counselling.

I found a useful website http://www.kent.ac.uk/careers/explorer.htm that you can use as a starting point where you can input your preferences to a list of categories and then click a button to ask for career suggestions.

Ask yourself
- What would you do if you didn't have to do anything?
- What activities are you happiest doing?
- Identify three occasions when you felt alive and powerfully you.
- If you found yourself in prison serving a long stretch – what would you still continue to do?
- What did you love to do when you were ten years old or younger?
- If you could treble your self-confidence what would it affect?
- If you could change three beliefs about yourself, which three would you change and what would be the effects? I used to say about myself, "I'm no good at remembering numbers," but I've since learned a method where I change the numbers into letters and now I have no problem remembering the numbers using this approach. It's helped with business, accounts, statistics and phone numbers!

"I'm always doing the things I can't do...that's how I get to do them," Pablo Picasso.

Invest in yourself 5.3

Just as the holistic community has a programme of continuous professional development, it is also advisable for your client.

It's a good idea to invest annually in improving your skills. Most companies have a budget for staff training and it would be worth approaching your company to see if they will assist you in the cost of any training. If they aren't willing, then invest in it yourself. If it takes you nearer your goals it is money well spent.

Get paid to have fun 5.4

I know when I was at school we were taught that you have to work hard for a living. It was many years later that I discovered that you could get paid to have fun! And when a job is fun for you, the old adage is true – you never work another day in your life. It's not that you won't work hard – you'll probably work even harder and put in longer hours when your work is fun, but you will never feel like you are working. That's the difference.

When your client has a gap between their second and their third toes you know that they are keeping their emotions out of it in order to get things done. Sometimes that can mean that they are trying to stay detached for a reason, but usually it's because they're not having much fun in their work.

Help your clients to explore what is fun for them. Could they change the way they are working to improve it? Could a change in attitude help? Is there a way that they can get paid to have fun?

I'm serious. It sounds quite trite but look around, ask around. There are many people who have a natural talent who spend a lifetime avoiding using it because either they don't recognise it as a profitable skill or because someone in their youth persuaded them to give up their dream.

I know when I gave up my day job to become a foot reader, there were people who said "You'll never make a living doing that." Happily, I ignored them and luckily I have a family who support me even when I am doing what appears to them to be foolhardy things.

Help your clients to explore some basics like whether they want to work indoors or outdoors, routine or non-routine, stability or adventure, big sums or big words.

If there's an ambition that you have but you talk yourself out of it thinking that it is impossible for you, ask yourself if you have heard of anyone already achieving it, if you know anyone yourself who has achieved it, or if you know someone who knows someone who has. Try to arrange a meeting with them so you can learn first-hand what they would recommend. What are the dos and don'ts? Learn from their successes and their mistakes.

When you get paid to have fun, it becomes less about the money and more about the process of being involved in it. There were times early on in my foot reading career when I was running out of money but the fact that I loved what I did kept me going.

I remember a time when I felt I was at my eleventh hour in my foot reading career. I'd nearly run out of savings and was discussing with my Dad whether I should get a part-time job to help tide me over. He told me that what I was doing was like surfing. "You're riding a wave, and you just don't know where you are on that wave. If you aren't there when the wave breaks then you'll have missed it despite all your prior efforts." Because my work was fun for me, I could see the sense in what he was saying, and I knew it was worth the risk of continuing. If it wasn't fun for me I don't think I could have kept going when times got tough.

Finding your passion can take a lifetime. I was lucky that I found mine in my thirties. Don't give up. Keep trying lots of new things. Quit early and often until you get there. There's a time to know when you're wasting your time and a time to be tenacious and stick with it. Recognise the difference.

Minimising the risk   5.5

One of the main reasons why people don't give up their day job to do the career of their dreams is fear.

I remember when I studied reflexology, I knew I wanted to find a way to make it my career. I worked evenings and weekends building up a practice. Even though I proved to myself that I could earn money from it, I still lacked the courage to take the leap from employment to self-employment.

I experienced all the typical self-talk such as, "But I'll never earn enough," "What if I don't get enough clients?," "What if I fall ill or take a holiday?" etc.

My advice is to understand what your fears are by listing them on paper. Not in your head. Physically write them down.

Looking at your fear, write down what one thing you could do to reduce or eradicate that risk.

I've done this time and time again with my clients. Firstly, writing the list down diminishes it somehow. When your fears are whizzing around in your head, they become larger and like a great big unconquerable mass. As soon as you list them, it's a way of unravelling them.

Secondly, looking the fears in the face, so to speak, helps you to start developing strategies to tackle them.

Finally, set a deadline.

When I gave up my day job I'd been practicing as a reflexologist part-time for about five years. I made my list, put plans in place to reduce the fears and minimise the risks, and I decided in the November that I would hand in my notice at the end of February and leave my job at the end of March. I told no-one. I decided to live with the decision – to try it on for size.

For most of November and December, if anyone cancelled an appointment I was in the pit of despair (what would this be like if I'd already handed in my notice?) and every time I got a new client I was in a state of ecstasy (what would this be like if I'd already handed in my notice?).

By the time January arrived, I had got used to the whole idea, the highs and the lows, and was so excited that I handed in my notice early.

I recommend setting a deadline and living with the decision, trying it on for size. For me, it helped me to know one way or the other whether it was a good thing for me to be doing, and I didn't have anyone else interfering with my decision until I was ready.

If you ask me now whether it was worth it, I'd tell you that I wish I'd done it years ago!

Reframing the problem 5.6

I could see from a client's feet that in the past she had really enjoyed her work and put a lot of herself into what she was doing. But more recently she'd stopped enjoying it. (Second and third toes on right foot were close together but on left foot were developing a gap).

Rather than telling her what to do, I told her what I'd observed and then asked her how she could change one thing to make it more fun for her. She explained that she had only taken the part-time role on to get some extra money for a specific reason. I reminded her that there was more than one way to get the money and that it was perhaps time to have a rethink. I gave her one of my meaningful looks and told her she knew what to do.

A few months later I met the same lady. She told me, "I did what you said." What did I say? "You know, when you told me that I could find another way to get the money." She'd reviewed all her outgoings and reduced them by changing providers, switching to lower tariffs and releasing anything that wasn't necessary. By doing this, she'd reduced her outgoings sufficiently that she didn't need to have her part-time job anymore.

There's no way I could have anticipated this as her solution, which is why I tell you to help your clients find their own answers. What I could do, once she'd found her own answer, was offer some additional advice to help her in this quest. I gave her the website for Martin Lewis (www. moneysavingexpert.com). He believes that the average family can save up to five thousand pounds a year by using comparison websites and cashback websites annually when their utilities, mortgage and insurances are due for renewal.

So when your client comes to you with a problem, learn to coax their own answers from them by reframing their problem.

I asked Simon Strong of human behaviour consultancy, Human Zoo (www.humanzoo.biz), for some ideas on reframing. True to his expertise, he reframed it as insight. Here's what he said:

What's the Problem?

An insight will illuminate the situation in order for action to be taken. An insight is the ability to see and understand a problem. Without insight, confusion reigns.

An insight results in action. Without action it is merely an interesting observation. Insights are a process of discovery and understanding. And a result of insight is change and adaptability.

So fundamentally insight is the ability to first understand the problem.

Digging Deeper

The more you dig, the deeper you get. And the deeper you get, the more fundamental the insight, the greater the change that is inspired. And the deeper you dig, the simpler, and more personal the insight.

A superficial level of insight produces blame and limited remedial action. The deeper the insight that we develop, then the greater the personal responsibility and the greater the possibility for creating campaigns for social and behavioural change.

Taking the idea of suffering a power cut whilst watching *Strictly Come Dancing* on TV and the idea that the more responsibility the individual takes, then the greater the move from personal change to social campaign:

INSIGHT:	POSSIBLE SOLUTION:
The trip switch has flipped.	Locate and reset. Blame electricity board for power surge. *No change in behaviour*
We are using too much power.	Turn off unused lights and machines on standby to reduce personal electricity consumption in household. *Change in personal behaviour*
The local grid is over worked.	Talk to friends and neighbours to all reduce consumption. *Campaign for social change*

The more fundamental the insight, the greater the range of possible solutions. Thus, simple business insights can drive initiatives for many years. The simplest insight could drive a business indefinitely.

The deeper the insight, the greater the consequences, and the wider the impact.

Whilst this is true for businesses, imagine how your clients can also be helped just through reframing their problem to gain a deeper insight.

Creating milestones 5.7

Where a third toe is shaped narrow at the base and wide at the tip of the toe, at work this person likes to start off cautiously, but as their confidence grows, they pull more and more resources to them, so that by the time they've finished they have overachieved. They probably would never have started it if they'd have known how big it was going to get.

With a person like this, it's useful to teach them how to create milestones. The more they successfully tackle a job, the bigger the next project that will be dumped on their shoulders. Teach them to break down the projects into smaller sections (milestones). Then only focus on one milestone at a time. That way they can still work within their comfort zone despite the size of the new project.

5.8   Planning versus analysis

When a third toe leans towards the big toe, the person is really good at analysing what has already happened. When the third toe leans towards the little toe, then the person is much better at forward planning.

As a foot reader, it's useful to point out their skill so that they can ensure that they are in a job that values their particular trait. No point being in a job that requires forward planning when your particular skill is quite the opposite.

5.9   Change just one thing

"How can we expect our clients to change if we can't even change ourselves?," a very exasperated friend asked me this after a long hard day working in the mental health sector.

He has a very good point.

Before you can change, you have to know that you want to change. Before you know that you want to change, you have to notice something that you'd like to change. Many people spend a lot of time and energy trying to be right, rather than just being aware.

Change is often what we want, but not what we are prepared to do. I remember when my Dad was trying to give up smoking. He said, "Giving up smoking is dead easy, I do it every day!" He meant that his aim is to give up smoking so every day he made it a habit to give up smoking. If by the evening he'd start smoking again, it didn't matter. He'd forgive himself and give up the next day. Eventually he finally managed to succeed a whole day without smoking. He's been smoke-free for 22 years now. He told me that although it's not easy, you know you've stopped when you say, "No thanks, I don't smoke." If you say, "No thanks, I've given up," you haven't.

The key to change is not necessarily the dramatic big gesture, but making one small change into a habit.

And notice what you focus on. If you say to yourself, "I don't want to be fat," your subconscious will hear, "I want to be fat," and your focus will be on eating. If you say to yourself, "I want to be slim" your subconscious will hear "I want to be slim," and start looking for ways to help you. With the idea of making one small change into a habit – if you want to be slim, go for a ten minute brisk walk a day. You'll find that after this becomes a habit, you'll happily extend the walk. Make it easy to start.

If you want to be rich, how much can you invest a month? Now do it every month. Or how can you spend your money on assets instead of liabilities? Or how can you create money from nothing? Find people who have done it already and ask them how. Learn from their experience.

Remember, a goal is only worth having if it encourages you to fall more deeply in love with your life.

I've been reading about how to stick to New Year's resolutions. Research showed a difference between men and women in their strategies to sticking to their resolutions. They found that men are better at sticking to it if the resolution is well defined, measurable and with clear targets. For a woman to stick to her resolution she would do better if she told everyone about it and if she wrote it down and put it somewhere prominent where others would see it. Perhaps this insight could help you alter your approach slightly according to the clients' gender when supporting your clients through change.

Chapter 6
The Fourth Toe

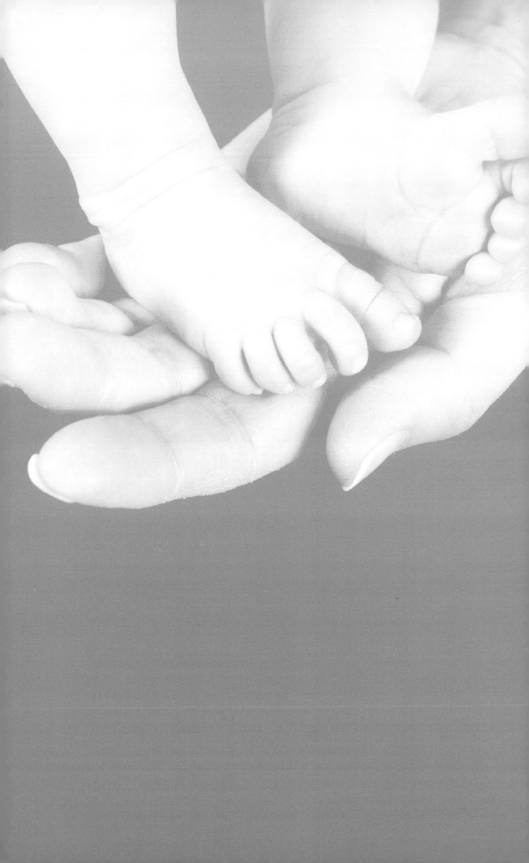

The Fourth Toe

The fourth toe right foot is about attachment to objects and the fourth toe left foot is about attachment to people. When read together, they are all about attachments, family, relationships, friendships and communication.

Be careful with the use of the word 'family'. It's about whom this person deems their family to be, rather than blood family.

Communication   6.1

Long necks to our toes mean that we are expressive. Short necks to our toes mean that we are not very expressive. Look also at the difference between how the necks look from the top of the foot compared with how they look from the bottom of the foot.

When the necks look fairly long from the top of the foot then they give the impression of being expressive and talk about anything. But when you look from underneath and see that actually, hardly any of the necks are showing because of the size of the toe pads or because the toes are held in – you have to have a rethink. This would mean that they may talk a lot but they hardly ever say anything about their own personal stuff.

If they are wide necks to the toes then they are very practical and down to earth but if they are narrow necks to the toes then they are more creative.

Communication – it's something we all do, but how many of us do it well? We talk but don't listen. We listen but don't express our point of view. We even say the opposite of what we mean. No wonder there are so many problems relating to communication.

Marshall B Rosenberg wrote the book *Non-Violent Communication: a language for life*. It's one of the most useful books I've read on how to communicate yet I cringe every time I say the title *Non-Violent Communication* because it immediately makes me think of Violence. (It's the brain not hearing the negative again.) In a nutshell, he advises:

- Say what you observe (without judgement or emotion)
- Say how it made you feel
- Say what you would like to happen next time

Accept that most of the time when people do 'bad things' to you, they probably had no idea of the impact you felt from what they did.

Understand that when these 'bad things' happen, you go into a huge mental dialogue based on very little fact.

I remember sitting in a café in the days when I had a normal job. There was a girl at the next table obviously sitting waiting for someone. Every time the door opened she'd look to see who it was. Then her cell phone rang. It was her date. Judging from her end of the conversation he was telling her he was running late. She flirted a little, and she also told him that she only had 30 minutes left of her lunch hour and if he didn't hurry up, he'd miss her. Some more time elapsed and he rang again. And again.

It seemed obvious to me that although he was very late, he was desperate to get there to see her even if it meant only for a few minutes. Finally he arrived absolutely beaming from ear to ear and only had eyes for her. The café could have been empty for all he knew, and he was hiding a gift behind his back. She too was pleased, even relieved to see him. But did she tell him? No. She began to berate him for being late. She ranted on and on and the chap looked totally crestfallen, the beam on his face turned into a glower and the very short time they had left was not going to be enjoyable for either of them. I don't think she ever knew about the gift.

She had a choice to react or to respond. She reacted rather than responded. Using Marshall B Rosenberg's technique she could have just observed 'you're late'. Fact. And he would have agreed. Maybe even explained why. She could have said, "When you are late I feel…"

a) Uncomfortable being alone in a public place
b) Worried that something has happened to you
c) Upset that I've used my lunch hour up just waiting.

He could have easily empathised with any of these things especially as she didn't say, "You made me feel…" because in truth he wasn't there to make her feel anything.

She could have then asked for what she'd like to happen next time. "Next time when you think you'll be more than 10 minutes late let's reschedule."

If she had responded in this way, her point would be made and they'd still have the good feelings that seeing each other generates and he's more likely to hear her, understand her and operate differently next time. Win-win. And my guess is she'd have got the gift too!

Another good book I'd recommend is *Time to Think: Listening to Ignite the Human Mind* by Nancy Kline which is all about how to actively listen.

6.2   Secret rule violations

Have you heard of the phrase 'secret rule violation'? It's based on the idea of how we go through life having unwritten rules and how we expect people to obey them even if we've never set the rules out for them. Obviously, if you don't know what the other person's secret rules are, you're likely to violate them! I first heard the idea from Michael Neil (www.geniuscatalyst.com).

Think about your relationship. Do you have any unwritten rules? For example, do you think that if your partner is late, they are being disrespectful (they may just think, "Oops, I'm slightly late," and wonder why you read them the riot act – this is a secret rule violation). Or think about the beliefs you hold about relationships. Do you think the man always has to pay or hold the door open? Do you think the wife must stay at home? Do you think a marriage necessarily means having babies soon after? Then consider whether your partner holds those same beliefs or not. Anywhere you differ could result, at some stage, with one or other of you committing a secret rule violation without even knowing what the other person's secret rule was!

Part of your role as a foot reader is to notice when such an incident may have taken place, given the story that your client may report. You can assist them by explaining about 'secret rules' and encourage the addressing of such rules through better understanding and of course communicating them.

Not so secret rule violation   **6.3**

An Iranian lady came to me for a foot reading but I could see that she had a particular question about which she was seeking advice. It turned out to be a relationship question. She had a male work colleague who wanted to become a friend, but who had no intention of marrying her.

I do not know much about this lady's country or her religion so any advice that I could give based on my own experiences would not have been acceptable and may even have seriously contravened the rules concerning her culture or religion.

In situations such as these, you know that at the most you can listen, repeat back how you have understood what they have said, then ask them what are their options. In this way they are heard and are able to explore their own situation with an objective stranger.

Through listening, I gathered that the rules under which she operated meant that she could not have male friends. The only acceptable male relationships were those with male work colleagues or with the man she intended to marry. There was no room in those rules to have a male friend.

Through asking her about the options open to her, she concluded herself that she would have to distance herself from the male work colleague.

I felt very useless in this situation, but I later received a card thanking me for giving her the opportunity to discuss it openly and to arrive at her decision.

6.4   Appreciation

If you're in a long-term relationship that has gone a bit stale, try looking for reasons to appreciate the other person. You get what you focus on and if you look for the bad, you'll only notice the bad. If you give out appreciation, you'll help revive the relationship. Remember why you fell in love in the first place. What one thing can you do today to show your appreciation?

I remember Caroline telling me that she spends lots of time and money on looking good, but her husband never pays her a compliment.
"Never?"
"Well, he did in the early days but not any more." I asked her when she last told him that he looked good. She reluctantly admitted that she couldn't remember the last time. Two wrongs don't make a right, so how about starting by *"Being the change you want to see."* (Ghandi)

6.5   Clearing clutter

If the fourth toe right foot is curved towards the big toe, then you have hoarding tendencies! You imbue objects with memories so that they become more than the object and it becomes really hard to let it go.

Whenever I see this, I recommend the book *Clear your clutter with Feng Shui*, by Karen Kingston. I don't recommend that you read it. I recommend that you open it at random and do what it says on that page!

Another tip is to check out the Association for Professional Declutterers and Organisers (www.apdo-uk.co.uk in Britain). There are links on the UK website for similar organisations based in other countries e.g. www.aapo.org.au in Australasia.

Example: Laura's Story
This story is written by Laura:

My Mum and Dad bought me a session with a decluttering lady, Louise Donald, for my Christmas present – I guess some people would have been quite insulted and a little aggrieved but I was over the moon as G and I are hoarders. We are both very untidy and the old adage of 'a place for everything....' doesn't figure at all (unless that place is the floor).

It took me a little while to get in touch with Louise and when I did it was after she emailed me – I think she must be used to clients being a bit sheepish about their homes! Anyway – we arranged for her to pop in one night to come and do a recce and then come back for a full day on 12th May. I told her on the phone that I wanted our bedroom to be 'a haven of peace and tranquility', and I asked her how messy the worst room she had seen was. She just laughed and said that she was sure our room didn't even come close. She assured me that I didn't need to do anything before she came so, of course, I had a mad tidy-round the day before she came to remove the surface clutter.

I liked her immediately – very practical, pragmatic and down to earth and spent time reassuring G that she wasn't there to throw all his stuff out (curses!). I showed her round the spare rooms and she said that we could do the upstairs cupboards as well to create space. Louise was clear that I didn't need to do any prep and that she was there to help me and do the graft while I and G would just be required to say 'keep' or 'throw' repeatedly!

What amazed me was how the pending visit of Louise affected me. The weekend before, I decided to tackle the cupboards in the two spare rooms – they had boxes that hadn't been opened since we moved in four years ago, or had been opened, looked at and then put back. What surprised me more was that I enjoyed doing the clear-out and in the space of a couple of days I already had about six or seven bags and boxes to take to the charity shop and three pretty empty wardrobes.

So, the big day arrived and Louise arrived armed with cleaning cloths (she cleans as she goes), bin bags, stickers and loads of energy. She suggested a very sensible approach that really wouldn't have dawned on me: ignore the surface mess and start with the wardrobe, cupboards and the drawers so that you then have space to put everything else away.

In the morning we blasted through the wardrobe filling charity bags galore and ending up with a wardrobe that actually now shuts. When we took a break for lunch Louise disappeared off with a car full to the gunnels with charity bags and recycling.

It was a bit strange at first – sitting on the bed and letting someone else do all the work.

What was great was that Louise just carries on at the point when I would have just given in – it took five and a half hours in all and when Louise left, the room looked fantastic. We cleared out a huge amount of stuff – most of it went to charity but Louise will also sell things off for you, recycle things and also uses the freecycle website for some items that she thinks will go down well on that. (Check out http://www.freecycle.org/)

I felt great after she had gone too – great to have cleared out so much stuff and I now have loads of space in all of the cupboards so I can tackle some of the other rooms in the house myself using the approach Louise suggested."

You can find out more about Louise Donald and her service at http://www.spaceandtimedecluttering.co.uk/

Decluttering Tips 6.6

Don't be tempted to start with the surface mess because that's usually the stuff you actually use or want to keep. Instead start with clearing drawers and cupboards so you've somewhere to put things away.

Organise according to your lifestyle:
Louise Donald says, "I had one client whose scattered clothes problem was solved by five laundry baskets, one or two in each room. Sounds a lot but it solved his problem completely, and laundry baskets look better than piles of clothes."

If you need an extreme declutter you could try something I found out by accident: Pack a suitcase of things to cover you for seven days and then go on a two month trip. When you set foot back into your home, you'll look at all the stuff in there and wonder why you need it all.

Each time you pick up an item ask yourself, "Does this add anything to my life right now?" If the answer is no, chuck it out.

Relationships 6.7

Ah Relationships! Maybe I'm not the best person to talk about this as I'm not in a relationship right now.

However, it would be very remiss of me not to include a section about relationships given that it is one of the most common areas raised in a foot reading.

Being realistic 6.7.1
Remember those fairytales we read as children. Prince meets Princess and carries her off on his white charger, and they all live happily ever after?

I asked around my friends about their relationships and fell about laughing at Sharon's description of the day the scales fell from her eyes. It was her honeymoon no less. She'd had dewy-eyed visions of married life incorporating nice house and rose garden. What she hadn't envisioned was on day two of her honeymoon, her husband handed her his socks with the expectation that she would hand-wash them for him! He countered with, "Why aren't you telling Jane that you sent me off, a green youth in a foreign land, to buy your feminine hygiene products?!"

What are your expectations of a relationship? Are they realistic? What are your prospective partner's expectations? Have you ever asked them?

As the old joke goes – women marry men hoping to change them and men marry women hoping they'll never change.

6.7.2 **The four pillars of relationships**
My sister recently went on a workshop and came back with information about 'the four pillars of relationships'.

- Truth
- Trust
- Voice
- Balance

The four pillars of a relationship are valid for any relationship – not just for your love interest. You can apply this to friendships, partnerships or even work relationships.

If you are assessing a relationship you should consider not just how you feel but also how you think the other party would rate your relationship.

Truth

Truth is, I think you will agree, an essential ingredient in a relationship. In the workshop that my sister attended, they asked 150 people to stay standing if they were 100% truthful with their partners. About five people stayed standing – on being challenged, they all sat down!

The point is not about being 100% truthful but being truthful on the important things and being truthful about what you both want from the relationship.

Trust

As for trust – there are many an example to show you that without trust, there can be no satisfactory relationship. If you trust someone then you are willing to converse with that person and share confidences, safe in the knowledge that the information will not be misused.

If you state that you will do something, do what you say. Keep to your word so that there becomes a history of trusting what you say you will do.

A survey carried out in 2007 for the drinks brand WKD revealed that we tell an average of four lies a day. That's 1,460 lies a year!

"Nothing's wrong – I'm fine," is the most frequent, with 28 per cent of respondents saying it was their favourite untruth. Next comes 'Nice to see you', followed by 'I haven't got any cash on me', 'I'll give you a ring', 'Sorry, I missed your call', 'We'll have to meet up soon' and 'I'm on my way'. Worryingly for women, the classic 'No, your bum doesn't look big in that' is the eighth-most-common lie. Lying about having kissed or spent the night with another person is the worst fib to tell, according to the 2,500 polled.

Voice

Voice is all about how you need to voice your concerns. There are many people who would rather say nothing than risk a confrontation. But this is your relationship you are talking about. How long do you think it can last if you don't voice your needs and concerns? Your partner is not a mind-reader. It comes back to one of my favourite sayings, "Every minute of every day you teach people how to treat you so if you say nothing you're teaching them that it's OK."

Voice is also about being heard. You can see this when the nail on the fourth toe left foot looks as though it has been squashed down – this person's ideas are not being taken into account.

If the other person in the relationship does not listen then it doesn't matter how much you talk. I know one wife whose husband regularly pretends to listen whilst thinking about other things so she has started to finish sentences with "...and then I threw all my clothes off and danced down the street." He hasn't noticed!

A little word about 'voicing': If you want a conversation, don't spring a surprise attack! Prepare the person for what you're about to say. For example, don't shake your partner awake at two in the morning saying, "You're having an affair, aren't you?"

Pick a time and place conducive to having a discussion. Say how you think the other person might feel about what you've just raised. It gives them the opportunity to correct your assessment.

Balance

Balance is all about ensuring that there's enough 'give and take' in the relationship. If one of you feels they are doing all the giving and the other feels as though they are doing all the taking, it's not going to promote a healthy relationship. How can the balance be redressed to both parties' satisfaction?

Frenemies   6.8

When the fourth toe on the left foot curves towards the big toe, then this represents how the person loves hanging around with people they've known for ages.

One of the problems with this shaped toe is that they see people as the sum of the memories they've built up with them, and forget to see how they've changed. In this way, it's easy for them to miss when a friend is changing from friend to frenemy! (That's a so-called friend who is not worthy of the term friend anymore because of their behaviour.) If they are becoming frenemies then this person will be the last to notice.

The tendency for a person with this type of toe is to give the person a lot of extra chances for the sake of how long they've known them.

I tell them, "See who shows up today. You've changed so much recently. Realise that your friends have also changed as much. Take notice and ask yourself 'is this person the same or different now?', so that you're actually looking for the differences. That way you'll spot a frenemy a mile away."

Chapter 7

The Fifth Toe

The Fifth Toe

The fifth toe on the right foot is all about fear and on the left foot is all about trust. Both toes read together relate to your sense of security and how you're going to move forward and take the next step.

Adventure versus routine   7.1

If you can wiggle your little toe from side to side separately from your fourth toe then you are adventurous. You need constant change and stimulation. You hate it when things become routine. When things get routine you'd rather upset the apple cart to see what is going to happen.

So if you have this wiggly little toe then you need to make sure that you have enough change in your life. If you always go to the café for lunch, make sure you regularly change the café that you visit. Try a hotel, or a bar, or a deli or a different café. Keep it fresh. Take on a job that is challenging and stimulating.

If you can't separate the fourth and fifth toes then you need routine for your sense of security. In this case, pick the 9–5 routine. Make sure that there is structure to your day.

If your partner has the opposite type to you, understand better how to operate around them. If you need routine and they need change, then give them the freedom to go off exploring on their own.

7.2 Fear

F.E.A.R. – False Evidence Appearing Real

When we were born, we only had two fears – a fear of falling and a fear of loud noises. Everything else we have learned.

No two situations are the same, yet we try to stick to the same reactions or methods or raise the same fears and objections when they are no longer acceptable for the new situation. For example, if you saw a poisonous snake in the wild, it would be reasonable to fear a bite from it. But if you saw the same type of snake in the zoo behind a glass case, it would be unreasonable to fear a bite from it.

It's important to notice the absence of events, not just the occurrence of events. In this way we can know that just because we won big money on the horses once, we won't necessarily win on the horses every time we bet.

There are different techniques that you can use to help alleviate fear: Emotional Freedom Technique (EFT), Time Line Therapy, and Cognitive Behavioural Therapy. If you are trained in any of these techniques you can use them or if not, refer the client to someone who does.

What is the opposite of fear? Trust. So if you can get the client to focus on what they trust in that situation then it can help shift and reframe their focus.

The past   7.3

Our brains are very clever. We have lived 365 days of each year we are on the planet and if we look back we can remember a whole heap of events that happened. Yet our brain is not remotely big enough to store all those memories. It does it by compressing the memories into a string of key features and when we access those memories through those key features, our brain 'fills in' the missing details. This means we don't really remember what actually happened.

It also 'fills in' when we think about the future. I invite you over for a Sunday roast. You picture the roast and you decide if you want to come for the meal. Now maybe you are picturing roast beef with Yorkshire puddings, or chicken with stuffing, or pork with apple sauce, or maybe you're vegetarian and you're thinking of nut-loaf. You haven't actually asked me what kind of roast it will be. Your brain has filled in the image of your idea of a Sunday roast. People who know me well may think, "Oh no! Not Jane's cooking!" based on previous experience. But without checking the details they don't know that I've arranged for someone else to cook. Maybe you are assuming that it will be a meal for two, or a meal for six. You haven't checked the details; you've filled in the detail. This happens all the time.

As a therapist, you are looking for the assumptions that have been made, both about the past and about the future, and are putting them under the microscope.

How much of your time do you spend wallowing in your past? Do you even know you are doing it?

A client who booked for a reflexology treatment spent the whole treatment telling me all about her past, what happened to her as a little girl. The whole time she was talking to me, I was wondering whether she was even feeling the sensations from the reflexology treatment. I started to wonder how much of her current life she was missing by focusing on what had happened in the past.

Now I'm not saying that what happens to you in life is not important. What I am saying is by getting stuck on that particular event means that you may miss all the rest of the good stuff that is happening around you right now.

How can you help your client to notice when they are doing it?

- *Interrupt* – I notice that you are talking about the past again.
- *Set the ground rules* – Today we are focusing on the present. Each time you refer to the past, I will interrupt/ blow a raspberry/turn my back/shout 'Fish'.
- *Focus on sensations* – What can you hear? What can you see? Ask about the senses in this moment.
- *Wrist band* – Get the client to wear an elastic band around their wrist. Every time they notice that they are thinking about the past, get them to "ping" the elastic band. The sensation will bring them back into the moment. Initially they'll be pinging away but once they become more aware of their thoughts the pinging will become less and less.

The method I use the most on myself is that of focusing on sensations. The first time I was invited to appear on television, I was so nervous. I was on the train, stewing in my fears, when I got a call from my friend, Simon Hathaway. He rang to wish me luck, but he could tell I was in a right state. He asked me how I felt.

"I'm absolutely petrified," I replied.
So he told me to look out of the window and tell him what I see.
"I see cows in a field, I see grass, I see trees."

What can you hear?

"I can hear talking, the sound of the train, a mobile ringing."

What can you smell?

"I can smell coffee and bodies."

In asking me these questions, I realised what he was trying to do. He was bringing me back into the moment, into what was real rather than imagined. So after his call I continued to identify what I could see, smell, hear and taste, all the way to the studio.

I remember it really clearly. I was about to appear on *This Morning* on ITV with Tris Payne and Lorraine Kelly. They led me onto the set. I could see the presenters finishing a live interview at the other end of the studio on a different set. All the time I'm thinking what can I see, what can I hear, what can I smell?

Lorraine and Tris sat down opposite me and I'm watching Tris pulling strange facial expressions and I'm staring at him fascinated, thinking why's he pulling that face? And then I realise that we are actually live on air and he's responding to Lorraine's introduction of me, for the benefit of the cameras. I reply to her question and it's too late to be scared. By staying in the moment and focusing on my sensations I didn't have time to get nervous at the studio.

Afterwards everyone told me how confident and relaxed I looked.

So from personal experience, I can recommend this technique as being successful.

7.4   Time Line

It would be useful for you to learn how to do time line therapy.

Andy revealed a fear of going over bridges. She had trouble walking over them, but as for driving over a bridge, she'd take the most circuitous routes imaginable in order to avoid taking a bridge.

Getting her to imagine herself stood on a time line with the past behind her and the future stretching out in front of her, I asked her to imagine hovering up and above the time line and to float backwards into the past. She hovered back to the time when she first remembered being afraid of bridges. Looking down on the scene from a safe distance, she realised that she had been driving to a funeral with members of her family in the car. There had been a panel missing on the side of the bridge and she'd had a fleeting thought about how dangerous it was.

She realised, when using the time line technique, that she'd associated bridges with death because the fact of the missing panel and the fact she was on the way to a funeral had become jumbled together and her brain had associated those key words together.

We did some further work on releasing, using the time line.

On my client's return the following week, I asked her how she was with bridges. Shocked, she realised that she had been walking over one only the day before and hadn't even given it a second thought until I'd asked her. She no longer has the phobia.

For more information about time line, check out *The Secret of Creating your Future,* by Tad James, and specifically chapter 7 on cleaning up the past.

Another technique for releasing fears that you may also like to investigate is EFT (Emotional Freedom Technique) which involves getting the client to tap on specific meridian points and focusing on affirmations. It's very effective and can be taught to the client easily. (See section on *Recommended Reading and Further Learning.*)

Money   7.5

People's sense of security often relates to the idea of money – the lack of it or the pursuit of more. According to a survey published by insurer Hiscox in January 2008, the UK's 'working wealthy' households earn £88,000 a year, have more than £20,000 of annual disposable income, take two foreign holidays and live in a home worth £390,000. What more do they want? The survey showed they wanted to earn around £60,000 more a year, own more than one property and send their children to a private school.

Nearly one in ten UK households are now classed as wealthy with the average wealthy family bringing in an income of nearly triple the national average, according to insurer Hiscox which commissioned the research.

Maybe it's not all about money. Those who have more than the national average still think they haven't got enough.

So before you put all your attention on money, consider this. Our time IS valuable. It's a limited resource, and most of us go through life treating it like it's not. Our time is finite. We'll probably only spend about 100 years on this planet if we're lucky. Every minute of it that we spend we can never get back. When you think about it like that, it's no longer a joke, especially when you think about how you choose to spend your time.

There's a film called *Changing Lives,* in which Samuel L Jackson's character shouts, "I don't want your money. Just give me my time back." Eek!

There are a couple of books I recommend to clients who come to me with money problems or who select the 'financial flow' card from my set of oracle cards.

Rich Dad, Poor Dad, by Robert T Kiyosaki, explains in a very easy to read way how you should focus on spending your money on assets rather than liabilities. Once you've read that one you'll probably want to read his book *The Cash Flow Quadrant* too.

Another book is *The Trick to Money is Having Some,* by Stuart Wilde. Once I had a stand at an indulgence evening in Buckingham where someone tipped a box of individually wrapped chocolates on my table. I was about to decline them, when I remembered Stuart Wilde's words about how money is all about being in the flow and if someone offers you something, just say yes even if you don't want it, so that you can give it away to someone else and thus be in the flow. So I stuffed the choccies in my pockets and at the end of the evening, I went around all the other stalls, offering the stall holders a sweetie. As I produced chocolate after chocolate from my pocket, I really did feel like lady bountiful!

If you prefer the more esoteric approach, you could try *Creating Money: Keys to Abundance*, by Sanaya Roman and Duane Packer, which looks at the spiritual laws of money and abundance through techniques, positive affirmations and exercises.

You could also look at Martin Lewis's website www.moneysavingexpert.com which gives lots of hints and tips on how to make your money work better for you.

Debt

According to the *Daily Mail* on 3rd January 2008, accountants Grant Thornton forecasted that there would be 120,000 bankruptcies in the UK in 2008. That's 10,000 more than in 2007. KPMG believe that this is an underestimation and could be as high as 130,000. Whichever figure is right, debt is a growing problem and it's useful to have advice and strategies to assist your clients as required.

According to the Citizens Advice Bureau, there are four steps to dealing with debt:

- **Make a list of all debts**
  Don't ignore your debts, they won't go away. Start a file to keep all the information in one place. List details of creditors, reference numbers, amount and keep original credit agreements with it.

- **Work out your budget**
  List your income and expenses for your household. Be realistic. Consider ways of obtaining more income. There is a website that lists organisations that give grants to people in need: www.turn2us.org.uk
  When you've listed all your expenses you can see if you can make any further savings (try www.moneysavingexpert. com) and then you will see if you have any money left over with which to pay your priority debts.

- **Sort out your priority debts**
  Priority debts are the ones where if you don't pay them the consequences are the greatest. These would include your mortgage (no roof over your head), fuel payments, council tax, court fines, income tax or VAT arrears.

- **Sort out your non-priority debts**
  You can't be sent to prison for not paying non-priority debts. But if you don't make any offers to pay, without

explaining why, then they may take you to court. These debts would include overdrafts, loans, hire purchase, credit card accounts and catalogues and money borrowed from family and friends.

Once you've sorted out these steps, your options may be one of the following:
- Making offers to creditors
- Debt management plan
- Administration orders
- IVAs (Individual Voluntary Arrangements
- Consolidation (putting all your debt into one loan)
- Asking to write off your debts
- Bankruptcy
- Negotiating with creditors

To read more about this, you can consult the Citizens Advice Bureau website http://www.adviceguide.org.uk/index/life/debt/help_with_debt.htm. They also offer assistance to help you budget, and to choose the right options for your particular case.

I did mention consolidation earlier (putting all your debts into one loan). There are circumstances where this may help, but please don't fall into the trap of taking out a high interest loan to solve the situation. This can lead to spiralling debt if you can't afford the payments.

Do not ignore debts – they don't go away.

7.5.1.1 Temporary Debt
Sometimes your client (or you) may need to get into debt temporarily. Most people immediately think they have to go to their bank or that other institution – The Bank of Mum and Dad!

Next time, you may like to consider a social lending website such as www.zopa.com where members can borrow money. In fact, if you're feeling flush with money and you want to help out others at a modest interest rate, you may also consider lending via the same website.

Luck 7.6

"It's a funny thing, the more I practise, the luckier I get," **South African golfer Gary Player.**

If you are polydactyl (born with an extra little toe) then you have a much stronger sense of security than most people and trust that everything will be all right. To the onlooker it would appear that you are very lucky. Polydactylism occurs in one in every five hundred births in the general population (but with an even higher ratio in particular communities such as the Amish community in the USA).

Whether you've got six toes or not, you can learn to be lucky according to Dr Richard Wiseman of University of Hertfordshire (author of The Luck Factor exploring the lives and minds of lucky and unlucky people).

He and his colleagues at the Perrott-Warrick Research Unit have studied over eight years what makes some people lucky and others not. He says luck is not down to kismet or karma. Instead lucky folk – without even knowing it – think and act in ways that create good fortune in their lives.

He makes the distinction between luck and chance as chance events being things you have no control over, like winning the lottery. They don't consistently happen to the same person. When people consistently experience good fortune in their lives, he says, it has to be something they are doing.

Here are four ways you can change your attitudes to become more 'lucky'.

7.6.1   Maximise chance opportunities

Lucky people are skilled at creating, noticing, and acting upon chance opportunities. They do this in various ways, which include building and maintaining a strong network, adopting a relaxed attitude to life, and being open to new experiences.

7.6.2   Listen to your lucky hunches

Lucky people make effective decisions by listening to their intuition and gut feelings. They also take steps to actively boost their intuitive abilities – for example by meditating and clearing their mind of other thoughts.

7.6.3   Expect good fortune

Lucky people are certain that the future will be bright. Over time that expectation becomes a self-fulfilling prophecy because it helps lucky people persist in the face of failure and positively shapes their interaction with other people.

7.6.4   Turn bad luck into good

Lucky people employ various psychological techniques to cope with, and even thrive upon, the ill fortune that comes their way. For example, they spontaneously imagine how things could have been worse, they don't dwell on the ill fortune, and they take control of the situation.

It's not what happens to you in life; it's how you handle it that counts.

Chapter 8
Nail Varnish

Nail Varnish

Nails represent protection of the way you are thinking. In my first book, *Let's Read Our Feet!* I describe the things that can go wrong with the nails and how this reflects external interference and one's reaction to that interference. In this chapter, I'm focusing more on how we decorate our nails.

When we decorate our nails, we are advertising what we want to attract more of into our life. It could be argued that, "Well, I only chose this colour because it matched my outfit," but any colour therapist will tell you that we are drawn to certain colours subconsciously at different times in our life. Looking back at my own life I know when I had a fibroid I was drawn to wearing reds and oranges, when I was in a difficult relationship I was drawn to wearing browns and greens and now I'm single I am drawn towards turquoise!

In 2005 I was invited to work on a press launch for a new range of cosmetics for Bourgois Cosmetics. As well as reading the journalists' feet, I would be reading their choice of nail colour. The fun thing about this was that even when the journalists got a bit squeamish about showing their feet and refused, I could still ask them to choose one of the nail varnish colours from the range and read what that colour would have said about them if they had worn it on their nails.

Red

The keyword for Red is Energy. Wearing red nail varnish indicates that the person is ambitious and would like to attract more energy.

Orange

The keyword for Orange is Joy. Wearing orange nail varnish indicates that the person wants to be the life and soul of the party! It indicates the wish to attract more fun into their life.

Yellow

The keyword for Yellow is Detachment. Wearing yellow indicates the wish to concentrate or the wish to cheer up and attract more happiness into their life. People who wear yellow nail varnish tend to be quick, bright and full of curiosity.

Green

The keyword for Green is Harmony. Wearing green indicates that you want more peace and calm. People who wear green tend to look for the best in everyone.

Magenta

The keyword for Magenta is Compassion. Wearing magenta indicates that you would like to feel better about yourself and be more organised. It's the colour for compassion and nurturing.

I've noticed that when a person has depression they tend to favour the magenta coloured nail varnish probably because of its quality for compassion and nurturing and to help feel better about the self. In colour healing, it is the colour used to help us let go of the past and change any habits that are no longer serving us.

White

The keyword for White is Completeness. White tends to be worn by people who are feeling stressed or are not sure about what they are doing. It's about wanting to attract more peace and to overcome problems.

Black

The keyword for Black is Control. Black isn't really a colour in the true sense. Black is what the eye sees when all colours are absorbed rather than reflected. People who wear black nail varnish want to attract an air of mystery around them, but also want to attract more self-discipline and order. It's worn by people wanting to ward off negativity or when they want to stand on their own two feet and face their fears.

Brown

The keyword for Brown is Comfort. Wearing brown nail varnish is indicating wanting to attract more comfort and security. People who wear brown want to feel safe or grounded and focused.

Pink

The keyword for Pink is Love. Wearing pink nail varnish indicates wanting to attract more love and affection into their life.

Gold

The keyword for Gold is Maturity. Gold is about being clear in our communication and positive in our actions. Wear gold when you need to meet new challenges and sparkle.

Silver

The keyword for Silver is Reflective. Wearing silver nail varnish means that the person is going through a time of reflection. It's a good colour to wear when you need to resolve emotional disputes and stay calm.

Turquoise

The keyword for Turquoise is Independence. Wearing turquoise is all about wanting to attract more freedom and independence. It's a good colour to wear if you need to be assertive in asking for what you need and wear it when you need inner confidence to succeed at something.

Blue
The keyword for Blue is Relaxation. Wearing blue is about wanting to attract more patience, perseverance and peacefulness. It's also about wanting to attract more truthfulness and honesty. It's often worn when the person wants to speak up for themself and keep their cool.

Indigo
The keyword for Indigo is Perception. Wearing indigo is about wanting to be more perceptive and intuitive. Wear it when you want to achieve something difficult.

Violet
The keyword for Violet is Dignity. Wearing violet is about wanting to attract dignity and to be respected for who you are.

Chapter 9
Using Cards

Using cards

When I first started giving foot readings, I would read absolutely everything I could find on the feet, then look up at the client, only to find that they were perched on the edge of their seat, waiting for more information.

They'd sought out a foot reading because they had a burning question that they wanted answering and the foot reading hadn't touched on the topic.

That's when it was recommended to me to try using an oracle card. It doesn't have to be any particular set of oracle cards, but it must be a set that you feel comfortable working with. Personally, I use *Healing With The   *, by Doreen Virtue.

I shuffle the cards, and fanning them out, invite the client to 'pick a card for guidance for now.' I read the explanation of the card from the book that came with the set. Sometimes if I'm pressed for time, I leave the explanation book with the foot party organiser so that the client can read and copy down the meaning at their leisure, leaving me free to continue the rest of the foot readings.

When I first started using them, I thought that it didn't matter which card a client picked, as they were all positive and would be a good way to signify the end of a reading. However, over time I saw that the chosen card would resonate with the reading, or with the burning question that the client had.

At foot parties, there are often themes running through the feet – indicating why they are cohesive as a group. At this one particular party, I offererd the client a card and when she showed me the card I said, "Why did you pick that card? It's not your card."

She admitted, "The other card seemed too obvious".

I showed her the reverse side of the cards, saying that they all looked the same on the back. If one looked more obvious then it was the card to pick. It's not a card trick.

This happened three times that evening with three separate clients. I learned a few things that evening. I learned to be more specific about how I offer a card. "Pick a card for guidance for now. Usually if a card looks obvious then that's the right card." I also learned that there is a right and a wrong card and not just any card will do.

And what I'm still puzzling over – how did I know that they'd picked the wrong card. As soon as they showed me, I knew it was wrong for them. Maybe it is because I'm so used to the card backing up the reading, or answering their question. Who knows?

The other set of cards that I use are the Inspiration Cards which I've described earlier, in the section about projection.

Using cards is a good way to bring out things that the client might want to talk about, that you didn't touch upon with the foot reading.

Chapter 10

Looking After Yourself

Looking after yourself

When you are working day in, day out, listening to everyone else's problems, then it's really important that you are in optimum condition yourself so that you don't start projecting your problems onto your client.

It's so easy to lose sight of what is fun for you when you are putting your clients first. I remember one foot party when seven out of the eight attendees were all counsellors and they all had the big toe bent towards the little toe – which in foot reading terms means bending over backwards doing too much for others and not enough for themselves. It's an occupational hazard for most therapists and it's something for which you have to have a strategy in place in order not to fall into the same trap yourself.

Take out your appointments book and put a line through two days at regular intervals so that you can't book any appointments on those days. These are your rest days. I know that when you get paid to do what you love, you don't want to stop – but you're not a machine and you have to rest to work at your best.

Now whilst your appointment book is open, also select some time for your annual holiday(s).

These days are now sacrosanct. If you don't take the time to do this now, you find you don't get round to it and that is a recipe for burn-out. Far better to look forward to your time off and enjoy it rather than lurch into it in a state of desperation.

I don't know what fun is for you so I can't tell you what you should do. What I do is go drumming. I belong to the Half Moon Drum Circle and I play Djembe which is an African hand drum. To me, there is nothing more therapeutic after spending all day listening to problems than beating the hell out of a drum. It's extremely releasing, it's healing and above all it's fun for me. My neighbour, Scott, takes great delight in asking, "Did you see Jane when she got back from drumming the other night? It's like she's been taking drugs or something. She comes back on a high!" No, I haven't been taking drugs, but yes, drumming is a natural high for me and a great way of resetting my system so that I can help others effectively. (And no, I'm not even that good at drumming! Expertise is not the point; it's how it makes me feel that is.)

Find out what is fun for you. What gives you that natural high and resets your system? Make sure you do it regularly.

The other thing I would say is, "If you want a magnificent life, hang around with magnificent people!" Who do you spend the most time with and are they supportive, inspiring, creative, and nurturing? Or are they draining, negative, and depressing?

10.1   Referrals

Don't forget – you don't have to see everyone!

As in all things, you are required to have judgement and discernment. There are some clients with whom you just don't gel, or with whom you don't want to work, either because you don't have the right skills, or because you've reached a plateau with them, or because you just don't want to work with them. Remember that you can refer them to someone else.

Probably the most extreme example happened when working in San Diego. I was working in a place where they charged me out based on time, and my client had only paid for fifteen minutes. I wanted to give him the maximum for his money so I (unusually for me) focused totally on giving him all the information I could in the time frame, rather than interacting with him. At one point I could see he was keen to tell me something. So at the end of the fifteen minutes, as I led him to reception, I asked him what he wanted to tell me. He glanced round, lowered his voice conspiratorially and said, "I'm really Nikola Tesla."

Croatian born, Nikola Tesla was born in 1856, died in 1943 and created and patented the foundation for modern polyphase AC generation and distribution. He was awarded 221 worldwide patents and 113 US patents. I concluded from this guy's claim that I did not have the necessary skills to help him further.

There was also the lady who'd been listening intently to what I was saying and when I said, "So next time you see someone with this kind of toe you'll know what it means," very seriously, she replied, "Oh no, I don't normally see feet. Most of my friends wear closed shoes." She paused, furrowed her brow, then said, "...except for those who dance around naked all day."

Know when to refer your client to others.

Chapter 11
Foot Parties

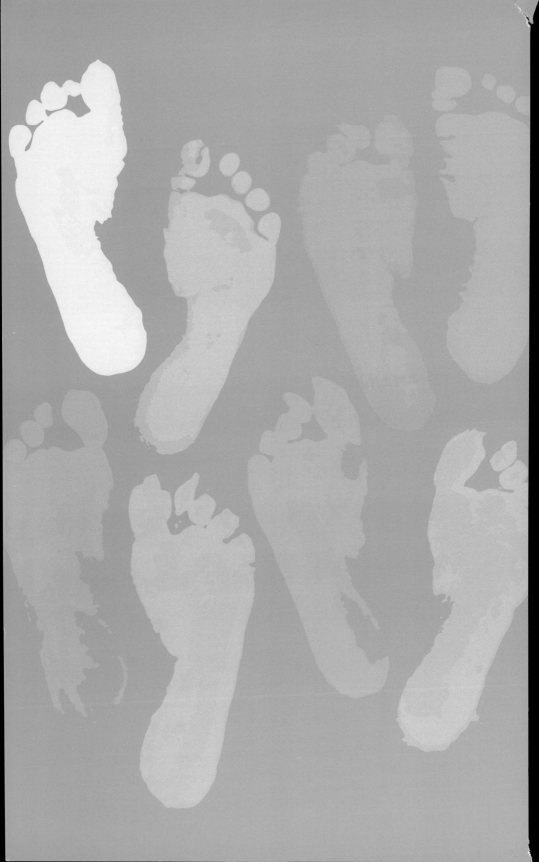

Foot Parties

I'm often asked what a foot party entails.

Usually, a hostess invites eight of her friends round for drinks and nibbles. I turn up with my reclining chair and stool and am put in a separate room to the partygoers. In this way I can see them on a one-to-one basis without disturbing the party atmosphere.

It usually takes me twenty minutes to get the person settled, read their feet, get their footwear back on and be ready for the next person. So theoretically I should allow three hours for a foot party. Yet it always seems to take four hours because someone has particular problems that take longer, or someone isn't ready, or whatever reason. It reminds me a bit of how in *The Hitchhiker's Guide to the Galaxy* they talk about Bistromatics – the phenomenon that mathematics takes on a life of its own when you try to calculate the bill in a restaurant. When doing a foot party the calculation of time allowed doesn't make sense. Eight people at twenty minutes each equals four hours! Go figure!

In the early days I used to collect the money for each reading straight after the reading from the client. However, I found it too disruptive so now I ask the hostess to collect the payment after each reading and pay me at the end of the evening. It helps with the time-keeping and helps me to stay concentrated on the readings.

And finally…

Saying Goodbye!

On a daily basis, we use our words to cast spells on people. You don't believe me?

I've noticed in England ever since the talk of 'war on terror' (and there's a spell being cast if ever I saw one – all you think of is terror after hearing that) there's a new trend that when you leave someone they say 'take care'. I'll grudgingly accept that maybe they are concerned for your wellbeing but I hate it! It implies that the world is full of danger and you have to be really careful out there.

While I'm on the subject, there are those who say 'Goodbye, drive safely!' Implying that you don't normally drive safely. The first few times it happened I'd sit in the car with my hands grimly affixed to the steering wheel expecting danger at every turn. How did that happen?

It reminds me of all those times I've witnessed mothers instructing their child who is carrying a drink 'Careful now, don't spill it' and as they say it, it gets spilled. What a surprise! You get what you focus on.

When I leave you, I'll say 'Have fun!' and I'd rather hear you say the same back to me than telling me to take care. Alternatively, I quite like the Star Trek greeting of 'Live long and prosper'.

Enjoy your foot readings, coach responsibly and with love.

Have fun,
Jane

Recommended Reading and Further Learning

Foot Reading

Let's Read Our Feet by Jane Sheehan,
ISBN 978-0-9550593-0-8

www.footreading.com

www.findafootreader.com

Language

The Structure of Magic: A Book about Language and Therapy v.1, John Grinder and Richard Bandler,
ISBN 978-0831400446

Communication

Nonviolent Communication: a Language of Life,
by Marshall B Rosenberg, ISBN 978-1892005038

Time to Think: Listening to Ignite the Human Mind,
by Nancy Kline, ISBN 978-0706377453

Happiness

Stumbling on Happiness, by Daniel Gilbert.
ISBN 978-0007183135

Weekly coaching tips
Michael Neil does a weekly coaching tip to subscribers on www.geniuscatalyst.com

Self-actualisation
www.micpeakperformance.com Mick MacKenzie's self-actualisation learning technique. Use my referral code of "foot reading" to hear the audio intro for free.

www.whatdoireallywant.co.uk, Simon Hathaway's coaching

Man's Search for Meaning, by Viktor Frankl, ISBN 978-1844132393

Time management
Do it Tomorrow and Other Secrets of Time Management, by Mark Forster, ISBN 978-0340909126

Clearing clutter
Clear Your Clutter with Feng Shui, by Karen Kingston, ISBN 978-0749918248

Money
Rich Dad, Poor Dad, by Robert T Kiyosaki, ISBN 978-0751532715

Rich Dad, Poor Dad 2: Cash Flow Quadrant, by Robert T Kiyosaki, ISBN 978-0751532807

The Trick to Money is Having Some, by Stuart Wilde, ISBN 978-1561701681

Creating Money: Keys to Abundance, by Sanaya Roman and Duane Packer, ISBN 978-0915811090

Luck
The Luck Factor: Change Your Luck and Change Your Life: The four Essential Principles, by Dr Richard Wiseman, ISBN 978-0712623889

Did You Spot the Gorilla?, by Richard Wiseman, ISBN 978-0099466437)

Psychic
Tricks of the Mind, by Derren Brown, ISBN 978-1905026357

Attack of the Unsinkable Rubber Ducks, by Christopher Brookmyre, ISBN 978-0316730129
A fictional tale about a psychic.

Releasing fears
The Secret of Creating your Future, by Tad James, ISBN 0-9623272-0-4

Tapping the Healer Within, by Roger Callahan and Richard Trubo, ISBN 978-0809298808

Depression
Food is Better Medicine than Drugs, by Patrick Holford and Jerome Burne, ISBN 978-0749927974

Acknowledgements

Thank you to every person who came to me for a foot reading and to every student who attended my workshops – I learned so much from you.

Thank you to my family for love, support, providing a writing retreat, playing 'devil's advocate' and for constructive criticism, advice and proof reading.

Thank you to Alison McCalpin, San Wearden and Heather Doyle for proof reading.

Thank you to my workshop organisers for helping to 'spread the love'.

'Jane Sheehan has her feet on the ground, her heart in the right place, her hands on the right reflexes, and a body of wisdom in The Foot Reading Coach *that will expand your mind and heal the world. Let your feet do the talking and read this book!'*

Mary Marcdante, author, *Living with Enthusiasm*
www.marymarcdante.com
www.bunionsurvivor.com

Index